Bumbleb

An introduction

Edited: Dr Nikki Gammans, Dr Richard Comont, S C Morgan and Gill Perkins
Design: S C Morgan
Contributors: Dr Nikki Gammans with Dr Richard Comont,
S C Morgan, Dr Cathy Horsley, Darryl Cox,
Sinead Lynch, Helen Dickinson,
Katy Malone, Aoife O'Rourke

Acknowledgements

The editors would like to thank Helen King for style and design comments and Ian Gammans for proof-reading some early versions.

We would like to thank the following photographers who have allowed us to use their fantastic work: Les Moore, Louise Hislop, Heather Angel, Peter Greenhalf, Paul Williams, Sarah Seymour, Dave Clarke, Nikki Gammans, Steven Reynaert, Nick Withers, Dave Goulson, Ian Beavis, S C Morgan, Nick Upton, Aoife O' Rouke, Adrian Cheeseman, Nadine Mitschunas and Jeremy Early.

A special thank you goes to Dave Goulson, Geoff Allen and Paul Williams for allowing us to use their illustrations.

Thanks also go to the Bees, Wasps and Ants Recording Society (BWARS) and all the volunteers who have submitted or verified records for BWARS or BeeWalk: we have used these records to create the distribution maps for the species accounts. Thanks to Mike Garrett for the pie chart graphic. Finally, a massive thank you to Steven Falk for allowing us to use his illustrations and so many of his stunning photographs and to Paul Wilson Patterson for design advice.

 ISBN:978-0-9957739-0-5

Published in 2018 by the Bumblebee Conservation Trust

Contributors

Dr Nikki Gammans

Lead author and editor

Project Manager
Short-haired
Bumblebee
Reintroduction Project

Dr Richard Comont

Editor and contributor

Bumblebee
Conservation Trust
Science Manager

Dr Cathy Horsley

Contributor

Bumblebee
Conservation Trust
Conservation Officer
West Country Buzz

Aoife O'Rourke

Contributor

Bumblebee
Conservation Trust
former South West
Officer

Darryl Cox

Contributor

Bumblebee
Conservation Trust
Senior Science and
Policy Officer

Sinead Lynch

Contributor

Bumblebee
Conservation Trust
Conservation Officer
Wales

Katy Malone

Contributor

Bumblebee
Conservation Trust
Conservation Officer
Scotland

Helen Dickinson

Contributor

Bumblebee
Conservation Trust
Surveys and GIS
Officer

An introduction to the Bumblebee Conservation Trust

The Bumblebee Conservation Trust (BBCT) was founded in 2006 by Professor Dave Goulson and Dr Ben Darvill after their research exposed serious concerns about the plight of bumblebees. In the last 80 years, our bumblebee populations have crashed, two species have become nationally extinct and numerous others have declined dramatically.

The UK is currently home to 24 species of bumblebee and the Trust is the only UK charity dedicated solely to the conservation of bumblebees. We are a science-based and evidence-led organisation and have strong in-house scientific and technical expertise. The Trust is at the forefront of reversing bumblebee declines with an excellent track record of practical conservation work, awareness raising and public engagement.

As a Trust, our vision is to prevent further extinctions and for a different future where our communities and countryside are rich in bumblebees and colourful flowers, supporting a diversity of wildlife and habitats for everyone to enjoy. As the first Trust publication, we want this book to become a constant companion to all those who love and cherish bumblebees, but above all, we hope you will enjoy it.

Gill Perkins CEO BBCT

Contents

CHAPTER 1

Bumblebee biology	10
Meet Britain's bees	12
The bumblebee's body	18
Parts of the body	20
The differences between bumblebees	21
Where bees are found	22
How bees evolved	26
How do bumblebees keep warm?	28
Bumblebee facts	30

CHAPTER 2

Bumblebees and pollination	32
Insect pollination	34
Buzz pollination	38
Crop pollination by bees	39

CHAPTER 3

Bumblebee decline	42
Loss of habitat	43

CHAPTER 4

Bumblebee habitat in your garden	46
Creating new habitat for bumblebees	48
How to make a wildflower bed	54

CHAPTER 5

How to collect information on bumblebees 56
Collecting information 58
Equipment to make recording easier 60

CHAPTER 6

The 'Big Seven' bumblebees 62
Less common bumblebees and cuckoos 64
Rare bumblebees 65

CHAPTER 7

Bumblebee identification 66

WHITE-TAILS

Buff-tailed bumblebee 72
Garden bumblebee 76
Heath bumblebee 80
White-tailed bumblebee 84
Tree bumblebee 88
Broken-belted bumblebee 92
Ruderal bumblebee 96
Short-haired bumblebee 100

RED-TAILS

Red-tailed bumblebee 104
Red-shanked carder bee 108
Early bumblebee 112
Bilberry bumblebee 116

GINGER-TAILS

Common carder bee 120
Moss carder bee 124
Brown-banded carder 128
Shrill carder bee 132

YELLOW TAIL

Great Yellow bumblebee 136

CUCKOO BEES

Southern cuckoo bee 140
Field cuckoo bee 144
Gypsy cuckoo bee 148
Red-tailed cuckoo bee 152
Forest cuckoo bee 156
Barbut's cuckoo bee 160

Finding out more 164
Further reading 165

GLOSSARY 166

INDEX 170

Different bumblebee species have different tongue lengths. We divide bumblebees into 'short' or 'long' tongue groups and they will forage on different plants depending on the length of their tongue.

Bumblebees have either a short or long face. Face length can help us identify different species. This queen Garden bumblebee has a distinctly long face.

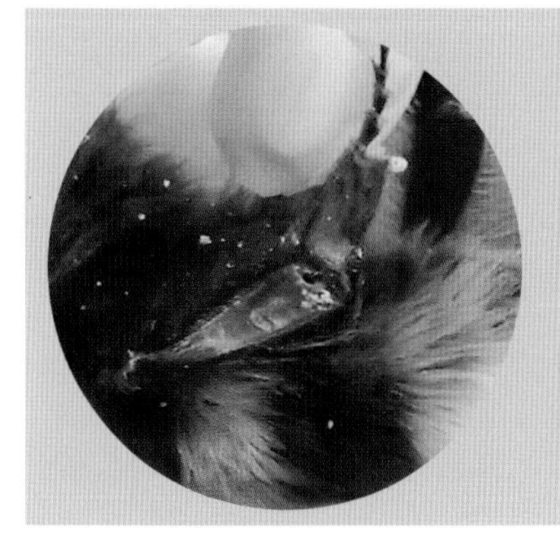

Queen and worker bumblebees store pollen on their hind legs. These pollen baskets are made up of a fringe of stiff hairs around a bald, flattened leg. The bee mixes the pollen with nectar and 'glues' the mixture onto the hind leg.

Bumblebees have thick hair and can warm themselves by shivering their huge flight muscles. This keeps them much warmer than other insects and allows them to forage in cooler temperatures.

Male bumblebees have longer hair on their faces. This hair can be bright yellow, which can help with identification.

Male antennae are longer and more curved because they have one more segment in each of their antenna than females.

Meet Britain's bees

Lots of people think that there's only one type of bee, the one that lives in a hive, dances and makes honey. In fact, there are three main types of bees: solitary bees, the honey bee and bumblebees. Together they make up the 270 UK bee species. In most bee species, the female collects pollen and carries it home to feed her offspring, but the lifecycle of each bee species is quite different.

The vast majority of our bee species are solitary bees and they nest alone (although nests can often be packed closely together). They don't form a cooperative nest and each female is independent. They make up roughly 240 of the UK's 270 species; in a variety of shapes, colours and sizes. The male solitaries emerge from their

Top Left: Honey bees
Above: The mating process for solitary bees can be quite abrupt
Below: A solitary leaf-cutter making its nest in a hollow bamboo cane

pupae before the females and their only goal in life is to mate. When the females emerge, the males find them quickly and mating takes place. Having mated, a female then looks for a suitable area to build a nest and lay her eggs.

This could be in a hollow stem, a crack in masonry or a hole in sandy soil. She excavates a cell and fills it with pollen and nectar before laying a single egg. She seals the cell, then repeats the process for each subsequent egg.

This provisioning is the only kind of maternal care provided for the young solitary bee. Alone in its cell, the egg hatches and the larva eats, pupates and emerges as an adult the following year. The flight period of most solitary bees is very short, usually lasting between four to eight weeks. The flight period coincides with the flowering period of the plants they feed on and thus pollinate.

There is just one species of honey bee in the UK and this is the domesticated one we all know. Honey bees usually live in a man-made hive and produce beeswax and the honey we eat. They also make royal jelly to feed their larvae.

Left: Honey bees are social bees that live in large colonies, usually in a 'domesticated' hive
Top Right: *Osmia bicornis* will nest in crevices and hollow canes

The honey bee lifecycle is a complex perennial round of making wax combs of hexagonal cells for laying eggs and storing honey.

There are two types of female honey bee: the 'queen' and her daughters, known as 'workers'. A hive has just one queen and up to 100,000 workers. The queen's role is to lay eggs and the workers' is to find food (pollen and nectar) for them. Nectar is collected during the summer and is dehydrated and stored as honey. During winter months, when it is too cold to forage, the colony uses this stored honey to feed themselves.

Top Left: Honeycomb
Right: Honey bees swarming on a branch
Opposite Top Left: Bumblebee collecting nectar
Opposite Top Right: Bumblebee nest entrance

The colony reproduces by swarming. This happens when the old queen is driven out of the hive. She leaves with several thousand of her workers to find somewhere new to nest. A new queen is then reared within the old hive. Once the new queen emerges she goes on a mating flight to attract males known as drones.

She mates with several drones, who then die, and then she returns to her hive to start laying eggs. If she ever leaves the hive again, it will only be when she herself is ousted and replaced in turn. Swarming takes place between May and July, which is the *only* time males are present in the hive: after that they are thrown out.

Twenty-seven bumblebee species have been recorded as resident in Britain. Three are now extinct, one of which was only ever a temporary

resident. Of the twenty four species remaining, eighteen are social bumblebees which make a colony with workers and the remaining six species are known as cuckoo bees.

Social bumblebees make a nest with one queen and between forty and four hundred workers, depending on the species. In spring, the freshly-woken queen looks for a nest site. Many species choose an abandoned rodent burrow that has old nesting material in it, which they use to keep themselves warm. Carder bees nest in long grass and use grass and moss to keep their nests warm. Many bumblebee queens are very opportunistic and you can find nests in compost heaps, under sheds, in empty nest boxes, loft insulation and even in old tumble driers.

At first the queen makes trips to feed and build up her strength. Once her ovaries are developed she starts to collect pollen and nectar to provide food for her first offspring. The queen continues to forage until the first workers are produced. They then replace her in the role of foraging. The queen will then stay in the nest for the rest of her life.

The first workers are usually quite small because, as larvae, they have only been fed on food collected by the queen. Later workers tend to be larger because there are more workers foraging and therefore more food to go round.

Bumblebees develop in four stages: egg, larva, pupa and adult. Eggs hatch into larvae, which eat the stored pollen and some nectar. The larvae spin a cocoon in which they pupate. The pupa is white and resembles the adult bee in shape.

IN SPRING SHE FILLS A WAX CUP WITH NECTAR, COLLECTS POLLEN TOGETHER, LAYS AND BROODS HER EGGS

SHE THEN FORAGES FOR NECTAR AND POLLEN TO FEED HER OFFSPRING

IN SPRING AND SUMMER HER WORKERS FORAGE AN FEED THE LARVAE AS THE NEST GROWS

A QUEEN BEE HIBERNATES THROUGH THE WINTER

EMERGING QUEENS MATE ONCE WITH AN EMERGING MALE AND THEN HIBERNATE FOR THE WINTER

The adult bumblebee finally emerges from the cocoon around six weeks after the egg was first laid. The queen continues to lay female eggs which emerge as workers. Near the end of the colony lifecycle at about 10–12 weeks, she starts to lay male eggs. At the same time, some female eggs are fed more as larvae and become the new queens.

For every new queen, there are multiple males produced. The males leave the nest first and never return. The new queens leave a few days later to find and mate with a male, often coming and going from their natal nest to feed on stored nectar.

If it is before mid-summer the queen will often start a new nest, but if it is autumn, she will feed herself up and then go into hibernation. The original nest she came from has now reached the end of its cycle and dies out completely.

A cuckoo bumblebee female is so named because, just like the bird, she will go into the nest of a social bumblebee and take it over for herself.

Each species of cuckoo bumblebee has a preferred species of host: she fools the workers into allowing her in and then kills or drives out the original queen. She then lays her own eggs inside the nest and lets the previous queen's workers provide for them. A cuckoo bumblebee does not produce any workers, just new females and males. These disperse and mate when they emerge from the nest. The new females go into hibernation to emerge the following year when they will try to find and take over a suitable nest.

Left: The bumblebee lifecycle
Top: Mating bumblebees
Above: Field cuckoo bumblebee

The Bumblebee's Body

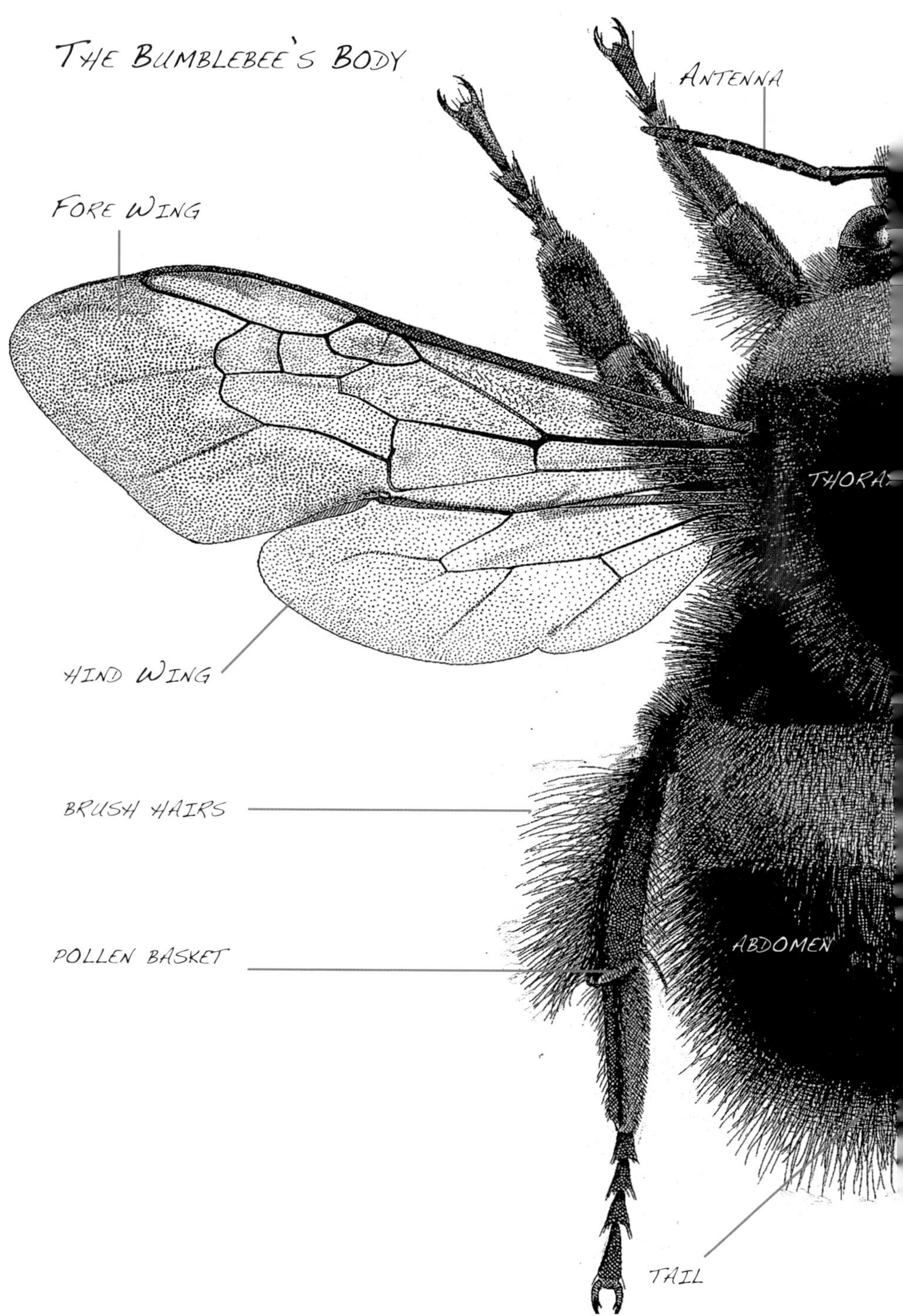

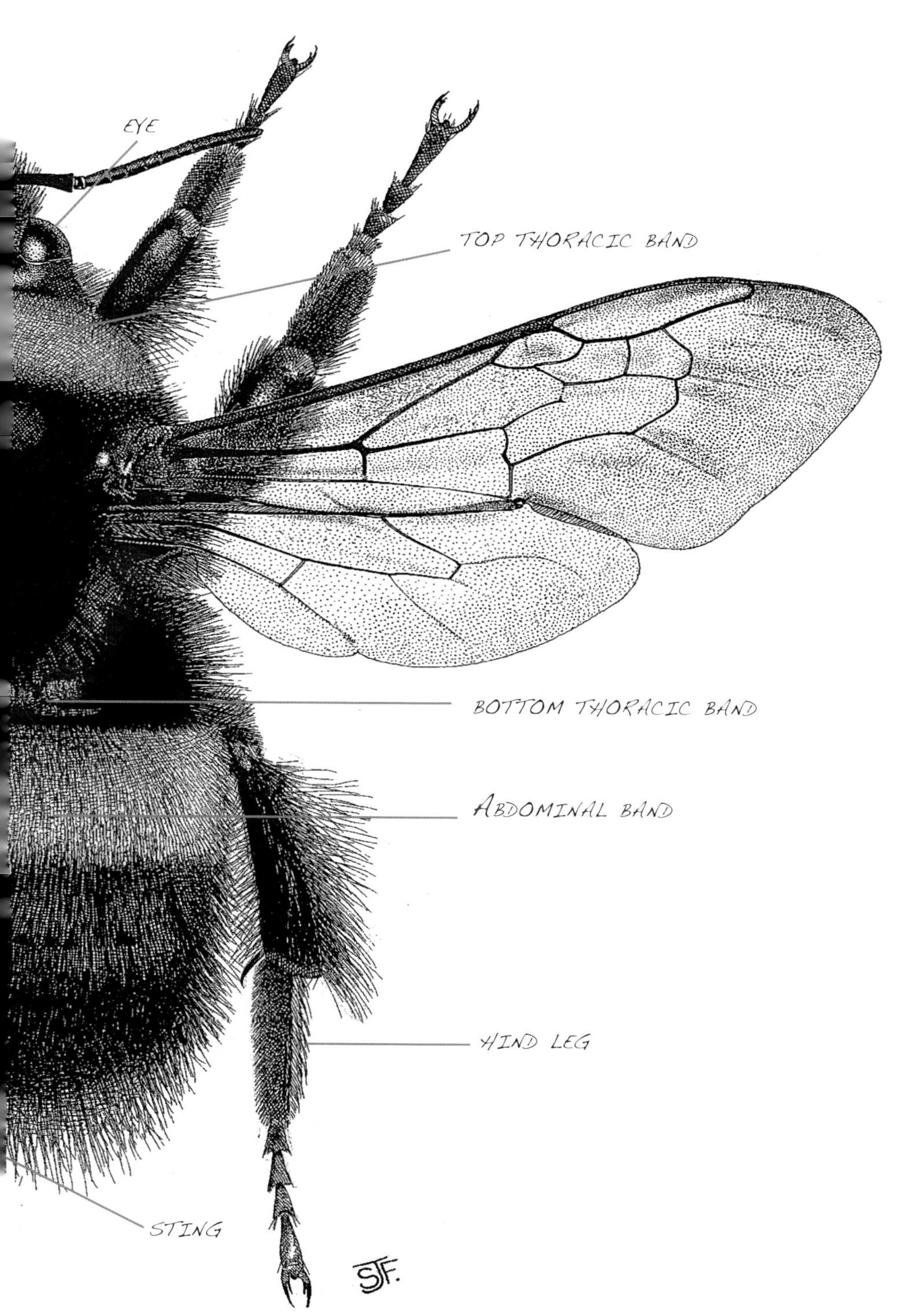
EYE
TOP THORACIC BAND
BOTTOM THORACIC BAND
ABDOMINAL BAND
HIND LEG
STING
SJF.

Parts of the body

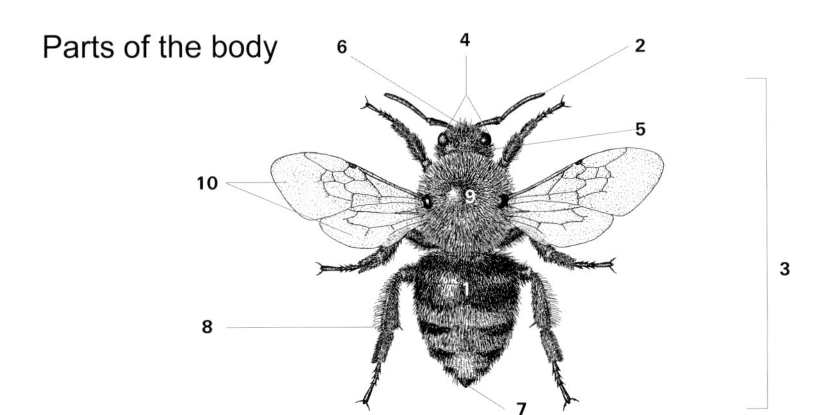

1. ABDOMEN The rearmost body section, containing digestive and reproductive organs.

2. ANTENNA Bumblebees have one pair, to detect the scent of flowers and other bees.

3. EXOSKELETON This is the hard outer shell which is made of chitin.

4. EYES Bumblebees have two large compound eyes and three 'ocelli' (light-sensitive cells) in the centre of their heads.

5. HEAD The front body section, with sensory organs and mouthparts.

6. MANDIBLES Mouthparts used to cut, bite, grab food, or use in defence.

7. OVIPOSITOR Female-only egg-laying organ, modified in bumblebees for use as a sting.

8. POLLEN BASKETS Females have these stiff hairs on their flattened, bare hind legs to hold the pollen.

9. THORAX The middle part of the body where wings and legs are attached.

10. WINGS Bumblebees have four wings: a forewing and a hindwing on each side.

The differences between bumblebees

Female bumblebee queens and workers have a different body structure to the males. Some of these features can help with identification.

ANTENNA
Female antennae are 'elbowed' and bent round the face. Male antennae are curved away from the head.

ABDOMEN
A female has six segments on the abdomen ending in a point (the sting) and ovipositor. A male has seven segments and no sting so their abdomens are blunt at the tip.

HAIR LENGTH
At the end of the lifecycle, the male moves away from the nest and sleeps outside. To keep warm, they have longer hair than the females which remain in the nest.

POLLEN BASKETS
Only females collect pollen and have pollen baskets. Males are often seen dusted in pollen.

COLOUR PATTERN
Males may have a different colour pattern to females of the same species.

DEVELOPMENT
Females develop from fertilised eggs and males from unfertilised eggs.

Cuckoo bees have some different features to 'true' social bumblebees. Cuckoo female anatomy is different to 'true' social females but males are the same, except for the hind leg.

POLLEN BASKETS
Female cuckoo bees do not have pollen baskets. The hosts' workers collect the pollen for them.

DEVELOPMENT
New cuckoo eggs are either males or females; no workers are produced.

HAIR
Cuckoos appear to have sparser hair and the chitin can be seen easily on parts of the thorax and abdomen.

EXOSKELETON
Cuckoos have a thicker layer of chitin on their body.

STING Cuckoo females have a longer sting than true females.

DARKER WINGS
Female cuckoos have darker wings.

TONGUE AND HEAD SHAPE
All cuckoos have a square, 'boxy', head and a short tongue.

Where bumblebees are found

Worldwide, there are around 270 bumblebee species, all in the genus *Bombus* - meaning they emit a deep, booming buzz.

The area around China and northern India is the most diverse, reflecting the *Bombus* origin amongst the Himalayas. Northern-hemisphere temperate areas in Europe, Asia and North America generally have good numbers of species, but this species richness declines as you move northwards into the Arctic regions.

Bumblebees *do* live within the Arctic Circle. In fact, they can be found within 1000km of the North Pole, but these species, the Polar and High Arctic bumblebees, are so

restricted by the short summer that the queens virtually act as solitary bees with, at most, one brood of workers. Further south, as you move into the tropics, bumblebees tend to be found only at higher altitudes where it is cool enough for the bees to fly without overheating.

Although there is a species which is native to the lowland tropical forests of South America, most bumblebees in the tropics are found in the Andes. These include the Patagonian bumblebee, light-heartedly known as 'the

Left: *Bombus kashmirensis*
Top: The largest bumblebee in the world (*Bombus dahlbomii*)
Right: A European species, the Moss carder bee

flying mouse'. This is the largest bumblebee in the world, with queens reaching 4cm long. Sadly this iconic species is at risk because of the artificial introductions of non-native bumblebee species.

The introduction of non-native bees by humans has been common in recent history. The European Buff-tailed and Ruderal bumblebees, for example, were introduced to Chile as recently as the 1980s to help pollinate agricultural crops including Red Clover, which was used was cattle feed. Much earlier, in the 19th century the Buff-tailed, Garden, Ruderal and Short-haired bumblebees were all introduced to New Zealand to pollinate Red Clover, grown as a forage crop for sheep and cattle. Unfortunately in South America the European bumblebees were imported along with several of their parasites.

Number of naturally-occurring bumblebee species for each 100km x 100km grid square worldwide

These promptly spread into the native South American species. As the natives had no resistance to the parasites they suffered badly from the diseases. An additional problem was that the introduced species significantly increased the competition for food.

Here in the UK, twenty-seven species of bumblebee have called Britain home over the past two hundred years.

One, the Apple bumblebee, was only ever a transient resident, living for a few years in the sand dunes of Deal in Kent, before vanishing. Another two species became extinct during the 20th century. Cullum's bumblebee was last seen on the Berkshire Downs near Newbury

in 1941, and the Short-haired bumblebee was last recorded at Dungeness, in Kent in 1988. At the time of writing extensive efforts are currently underway to reintroduce the Short-haired bumblebee at Dungeness. Along with six other species, which is more than a quarter of all British bumblebees, it remains on the list of UK priority species for conservation.

One species *hasn't* waited for human intervention. The Tree

bumblebee crossed the Channel from Europe and was first recorded in southern England in 2001. It has spread rapidly across Britain reaching Land's End in 2010 and Scotland in 2013.

The Tree bumblebee is mainly found in urban and suburban areas where it forages from a wide range of garden and meadow plants. It prefers to nest high above ground in bird boxes and roof cavities. This behaviour is completely unlike any other British bumblebee species and so it has virtually no competition for nest sites.

It is now one of the most widespread and abundant species across the country. The spread of the Tree bumblebee is a rare good news story amongst so many examples of decline.

Opposite Left: The Apple bumblebee
Opposite Top Right: Cullum's bumblebee
Opposite Bottom Right: A Ruderal bumblebee - this is a dark form with no coloured bands and black hair throughout
Top Left: The Short-haired bumblebee
Above: Tree bumblebees in a nest box
Left: A Tree bumblebee with its distinctive brown, black and white markings

How bees evolved

It is widely thought that bees evolved about 130 million years ago. The very first bees evolved from predatory, carnivorous wasps. Over time, these early wasps changed their diets. Instead of collecting other insects to feed their young, they began collecting pollen. Over thousands of years, this change in diet led to the evolution of what we know as bees. Bees are now herbivorous and feed only on pollen and nectar.

This one dietary change has had a profound impact on the world we see today.

Bees evolved at approximately the same point in history as that at which flowering plants also began

to evolve on a mass scale. This flourishing relationship between bees and flowers has resulted in 20,000 different bee species and around 400,000 flowering plant species with many plants evolving special markings and shapes to attract bees.

Several of the earliest bees have been preserved in amber and fossilised. The oldest fossilised bee was found in 2006 and dates back one hundred million years. This ancient fossil species shares a number of both wasp

Left: Bumblebee foraging for pollen with loaded pollen baskets
Top Right: Many of our vast number of flower species evolved from a relationship with bees

and bee features and has been hugely important in helping us to understand the evolutionary history of bees. It is believed that bumblebees evolved in the Himalayas, in Asia, around twenty five to forty million years ago. This area still has the greatest bumblebee diversity today. Bumblebees originally evolved to live in the cooler temperatures of mountainous territory and are thought to have spread from Asia following a period of global cooling.

From the high Himalayas they continued to spread across Eurasia and even to the North American continent. Eventually bumblebees crossed the equator in the Americas through the cool mountain ridges of the Andes and eventually populated the southern hemisphere.

This spread of bees across so many different habitats has resulted in the diversification of bumblebee species. There are over 270 bumblebee species in total: all of them specially adapted so that they can thrive in their own particular environment.

Below: Bees evolved to survive in the cold conditions of the Himalayas

How do bumblebees keep warm?

Insects are cold-blooded animals which means that, unlike us, they cannot control their own body temperature. They need the sun to warm them up when it is cool and they need shade to cool them down when it is too hot. However, bumblebees act much more like warm-blooded animals than most other insects. This is because they use a variety of techniques like shivering their wing muscles and altering how they pump warm and cool blood around their body sections to change their body temperature.

Most insects need warm weather to warm their muscles up enough to fly but bumblebees can fly at an air temperature of 10°C or less. This is a temperature 4-5°C

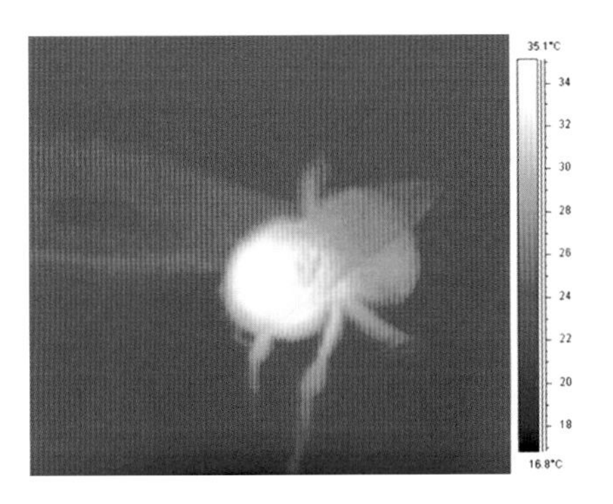

lower than that at which honeybees and solitaries can fly. So how do they do it?

Firstly, bumblebees can dislocate their wings from their wing muscles and shiver them to warm up. Shivering is, in fact, what mammals do to keep warm: when we get cold we begin to shiver. Bumblebees also have furry bodies and this hair acts as insulation to keep them warm. When it is too hot they increase the amount of hot blood pumped into the abdomen, which is expanded as far as it will go to increase the surface area, thus venting heat more quickly.

This pushes out the hot air and cools down the body like air conditioning. Bumblebees tend to nest in south and south-east facing sites. This means they get the morning sun to help them warm up. They hibernate, however, in north-facing areas to avoid being woken up too early from their sleep by warm weather!

Opposite Top Left: Bumblebees can even fly in frosty weather
Opposite Bottom Left: An ability to emerge early means they can take advantage of early flowers like crocuses
Top Left: Infrared photograph showing the heat produced by a bee in flight (white is hot)
Left: Bumblebee's wings in flight
Above: The bee's thick hair protects it from the cold

Bumblebee facts

According to physics bumblebees should not be able to fly.

This is an apocryphal story which assumes that bumblebees fly, like a plane, without moving their wings. Bumblebee wings rotate in a figure-8 shape as they are flapped up to 200 times per second, flying more like a helicopter than a plane.

Do bumblebees sting?

Some do, some don't. All female bumblebees - queens and workers can sting, but males can't - they don't physically have a sting. Bumblebees are fairly docile and most will only sting if they think they are under threat. If they raise a leg at you they are not happy.

Do bumblebees die if they sting you?

No: only honey bees die after stinging. They have a barbed sting which gets stuck in whatever they've stung, pulling the back end out of the bee as it flies away. Solitary and bumblebees have unbarbed stings. They withdraw the sting and so don't die.

Bumblebee workers can carry up to 77% of their own bodyweight in pollen and nectar.

That's the equivalent of a 10 stone man carrying around an average-sized 14 year old boy.

Bumblebees must drink nectar approximately every 40 minutes when flying. When their honey stomach (a section of the digestive system used to carry nectar) is full, this only gives them 40 minutes of flight. If you see a worn-out bee, mix some sugar and water together and offer it to the bee on a teaspoon. Otherwise place the bee on a flower so it can drink.

Flowers attract bees using scents, bright colours and ultra-violet 'landing strips' which guide them to the nectar.

Their petals have microscopic textures to help bees grip.

Over millennia, many flowers have developed sweet nectar and plenty of pollen with which to attract bees and other pollinators.

Female bumblebees collect pollen and brush it into their pollen baskets as food for their offspring. The fine hairs on the bees body also collect pollen 'accidentally' and transfer it from flower to flower. In this way males can also act as pollinators.

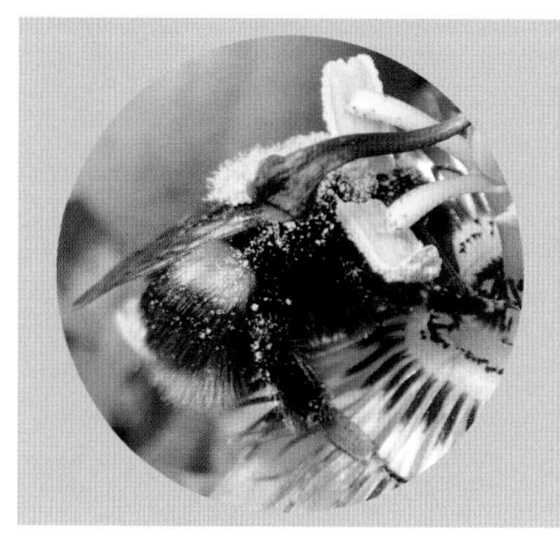

Some plants have developed very complex structures to deposit their pollen on passing bees. This Passion Flower has angled anthers, which daub pollen onto the bee's back as it drinks nectar.

Plants with open, uncomplicated flowers make it easy for bees to collect pollen and nectar. Those with 'double' flowers that have many curled-in petals often produce little nectar or pollen, so are of little value to pollinators.

In summer, some plants produce so much nectar it is possible to see many bees on one composite flower head. If you see lots of lazy-looking bees in late summer, lolling about on flowers, they may well be nectaring males.

Different plants have different coloured pollen. These range from the dark purple of poppies through to bright orange (see *Hypericum* pollen right) to pale yellow, grey and white.

Insect pollination

Pollination is the process of plant sexual reproduction. Cross-pollination occurs when pollen grains (the plant's male reproductive cells) are transferred from the male anther of one flower to the female stigma of another flower of the same species.

Once it has landed on the stigma, the pollen grain germinates and grows a pollen tube down through the style towards the flower's ovary. The ovary contains the plant's female reproductive cells. When the pollen tube reaches the ovary and the male and female reproductive cells meet, fertilisation takes place. The fertilised ovules develop into seeds and the ovary develops into a fruit which sits around the seeds. Because plants have roots and are fixed to their growing spot they require help in moving pollen from flower to flower. Pollination can occur when the pollen is transported by wind or water. It can also occur when the pollen is transferred by an animal, such as an insect or bird.

Most flowering plants are pollinated by insects. These pollinators include many different species of bees, flies, wasps, butterflies, moths and beetles. Bumblebees are some of the most important of these pollinators in temperate regions.

Plants have evolved a variety of mechanisms to attract pollinators. These include colour, ultra-violet patterns, shape, scent and, most importantly, a food source. Plants provide pollen (protein-rich) and nectar (sugar-rich), which

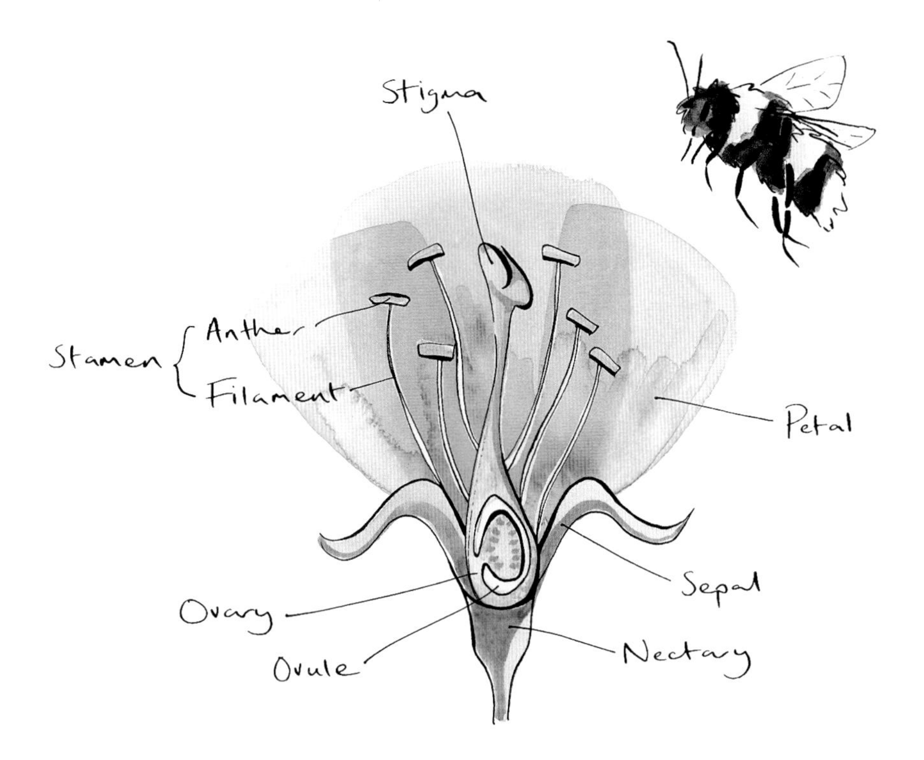

bumblebees have evolved to use exclusively as their source of nutrition. Whilst busy feeding on nectar and collecting pollen, bumblebees help pollination by unintentionally transferring pollen from one flower to another. This happens because the pollen sticks to their hairy bodies and brushes off on the next flower they visit. When they are collecting pollen deliberately bees use the plant's nectar as a type of glue. This combines with the pollen grains to form solid clumps which they carry on their hind legs.

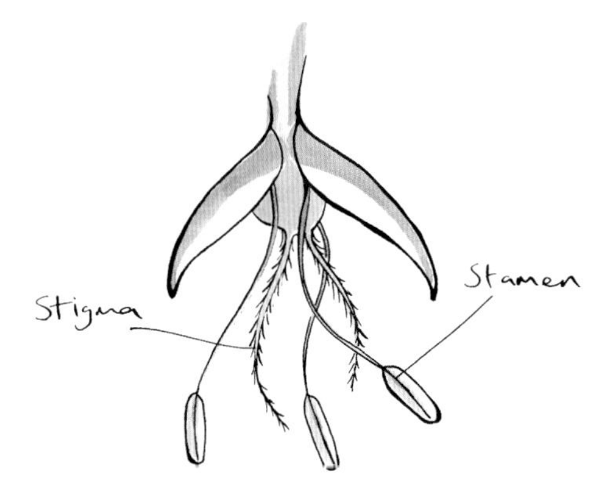

Bottom Left: *Syrphus vitripennis*
Bottom Centre: Chalk-hill Blue
Bottom Right: Wasp Beetle
Top: Interior of flower, insect-pollinated
Above: Wind-pollinated plant interior

Certain flowers have evolved so they can only be pollinated by bumblebees. Some of them have, for example, tightly packed pollen, which can only be dislodged by bumblebees. Sometimes they develop long trumpet-like flowers where nectar can only be reached by long-tongued bumblebees. Bees are responsible for a large part of pollination, but different bees

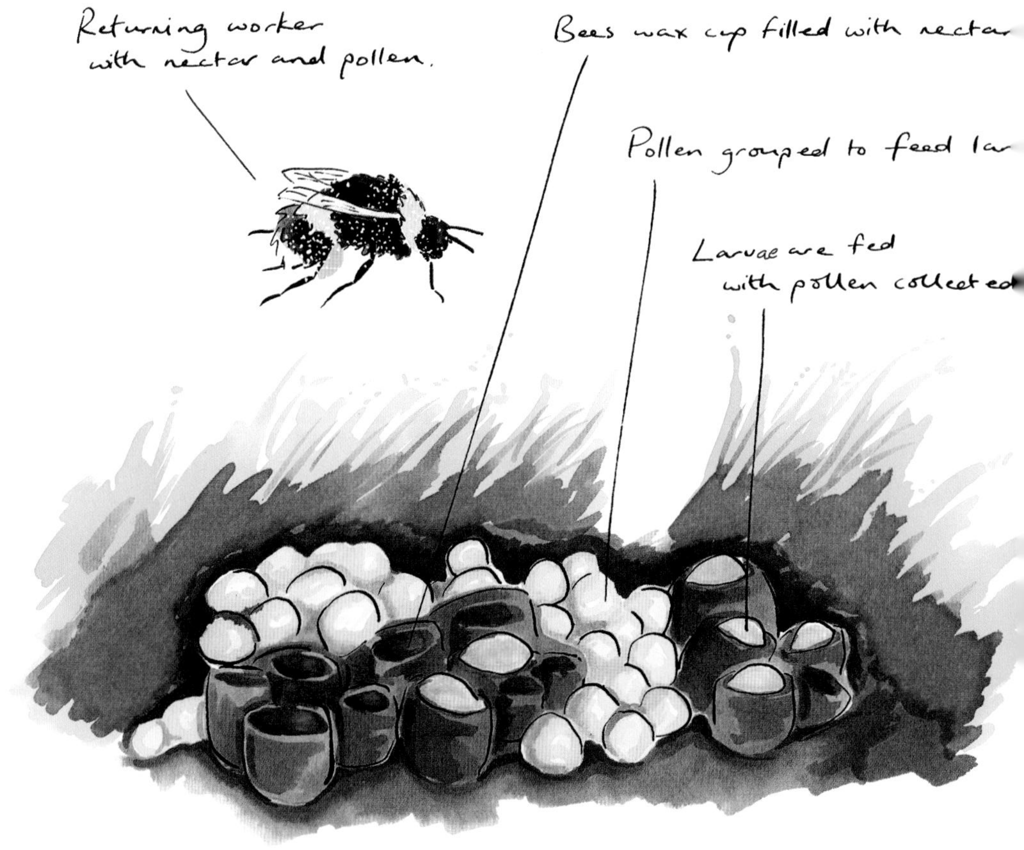

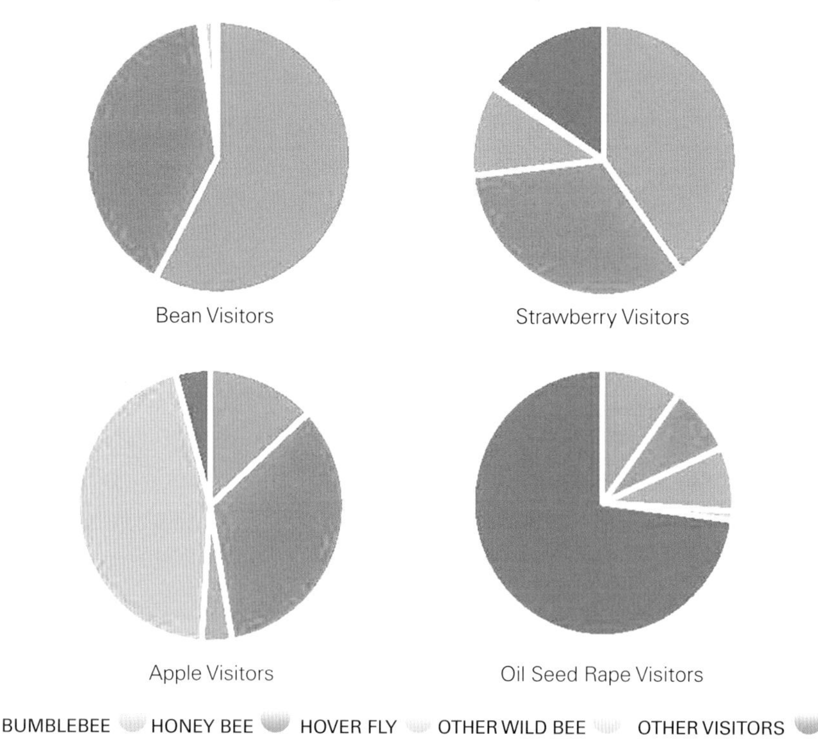

pollinate different crops, shown in the pie charts above. It is therefore important to save all our bees and other insect pollinators because they play a crucial role in preserving complex ecosystems such as wild flower meadows and agriculture.

Bumblebees pollinate fruits and vegetables including raspberries, strawberries, peas, beans, blueberries and tomatoes. Tomatoes require a very specific type of pollination to produce the best fruit. In the UK, only bumblebees can perform this type of pollination.

Opposite Top Right: Long-tongued bumblebees thrive on the Foxglove's trumpet-like flowers
Opposite Bottom: How bees use pollen and nectar to feed their young
Above: Pie charts show the numbers of bees visiting each plant

Buzz-pollination

Bumblebee species are some of the few in Europe capable of 'buzz-pollination' or sonication. Buzz-pollination is a necessary process for over 20,000 species of plant around the world, including important crops like tomatoes, aubergines, kiwis and blueberries. These plants keep their pollen held very tightly in their anthers. In order for the pollen to be released a visitor needs to really vibrate these anther cones to shake the pollen free.

Bumblebees can do this by grabbing hold of the flower with their mouth parts, dislocating their wings and rapidly vibrating their flight muscles.

Shaking the anther like this causes the flower to release a shower of pollen grains all over the bee's body and the bee then combs these pollen grains into her pollen baskets. Some grains will inevitably be missed and will go on to be deposited accidentally on to one of the next flowers the bee visits, thus pollinating it in the process.

Unlike honeybees and many other bee species, bumblebees will fly quite happily under the cover of glass houses and poly-tunnels, making them ideal pollinators for commercial soft-fruit growers. Their special abilities have led to bumblebees being reared commercially in artificial nests and placed in commercial environments to aid the pollination of soft fruit. This enables farmers to extend the growing season and produce higher yields. For this reason, artificial bumblebee nests have been exported all over the world. The UK soft fruit industry currently imports approximately 65,000 bumblebee nests per year.

Crop pollination by bees

About 90% of all flowering plants are believed to be pollinated by animals, mostly by insects. A very large diversity of animal species, around 300,000 worldwide, visit flowering plants. Bees make up approximately 10% of these species and rely entirely on flowering plants for their food throughout their lifecycle. This makes them an important pollinator group. Despite the fact that there are many different types of pollinators, bees are, without doubt, the most important, both ecologically and economically around the world. In the absence of enough animal pollinators, some plants resort to 'self-pollination', which can lead to deformed fruit. Estimates suggest that animal pollinators are important for a third of global crop production. At least 60-80% of wild plant species rely on animal pollinators.

A decline in the number of pollinators could affect crop yield and even food prices in the long term. Bumblebees are essential for a healthy environment and for successful agriculture in the UK.

Opposite Left: Blueberries are one of the crops that need buzz-pollination
Top Left: Self-pollinated strawberries can develop lumps and bumps
Above: Tomatoes rely on buzz-pollination

To give some idea of the extent of their importance it is possible to put an economic value on insect pollination. In monetary terms, the value of pollinators to UK farming was £440 million per year in 2010. This figure had grown to over £691 million per year in 2015.

It has been proven that the success of the farming economy is strongly linked with pollinators. So what can be done about pollinator decline? Some people have suggested replacing insect pollinators with schemes as high-tech as using tiny pollinator robots. Others have suggested low-tech alternatives such as hand-pollinating. This is carried out in parts of China where the over-use of chemicals has eradicated the local bee population. To hand-pollinate crops in Britain would involve a large army of people and estimates put the cost to the economy at an unsustainable £1.8 billion per year. The best solution is to make farming more sustainable by simply helping all the insect pollinators in our countryside to maintain food production.

We mentioned earlier that the biggest threat to pollinators is habitat loss and this bears repetition. Today the UK has just 3% of the ancient wild flower meadows we had only 80 years

Above: Bumblebee pollinating field beans

Right: Runner beans need insect pollinators

ago. This loss has resulted in a catastrophic reduction of available forage and nesting sites.

As a way of creating more habitat the government currently offers payment schemes to farmers from the European Common Agricultural Policy to encourage them to leave land aside for wildlife. To help our pollinators this involves the restoration of hay meadows and the introduction of low-input grazing. The 'low-input' approach promotes a method of managing grasslands so that there is a restriction of fertilizers and controlled grazing. The result is a much more diverse type of pasture. It also involves creating pollen and nectar strips around arable fields and management of hedgerows to provide more forage and nesting sites. Farmers can sign up to these national schemes and are paid annually for doing so. These schemes have been found to be greatly successful in increasing the populations of many rare species such as the Ruderal, Brown-banded and Moss carder bees.

Below: An 'agri-environment' scheme field showing the wild flower strip at the side

Your back garden can be a real haven for bees. Simply by growing some bee-friendly plants like Borage, Lavender, Foxgloves and *Calendula*, you can provide useful forage for bees.

The Buff-tailed bumblebee will have a colony cycle over the winter months of the year in the south of England. Planting flowers like *Mahonia*, hellebores, Alpine Heather and Winter Honeysuckle will attract them to your garden.

Modern farming, with its reliance on monoculture, chemical pesticides and fertilisers, offers little help to bees. Farmers can now sign up to schemes to help wildlife, including pollinators.

Loss of habitat

Many bumblebee species have suffered a serious long-term decline. There are many reasons for this but the main one is the loss of 97% of our ancient wild flower meadows. The devastation of our meadows has caused a disastrous reduction of forage and nesting sites for our bumblebees.

The loss started during World War II when the need for home-grown food led to intensive farming across the country. The 'Dig for Victory' campaign encouraged people to dig up their meadows, flowerbeds and lawns to grow vegetables to supplement their rations. The campaign fed the nation, but changed the landscape forever.

Ancient flower-rich meadows, once bumblebee havens, were replaced with crops and productive fast-growing grasses to feed livestock. Increased agricultural efficiency, through newly-mechanised farm machinery, cheap fertilisers and pesticides,

Top Left : World War II poster encouraging vegetable production
Above: Traditional farming with wild flowers mixed into the crop

with a production-based subsidy system led to even more intensive farming. After the end of World War II there was a boom in the population, resulting in increased urbanisation. This in turn led to the further reduction of our wild, open spaces. Today bumblebees are now under threat from exposure to 'new' pesticides such as neonicotinoids. The effects on bees are still being researched but we know that some pesticides can reduce a bee's ability to gather food, can hinder their navigation and can slow colony growth and larval development.

In nature, bumblebee numbers are lowered by many predators, which eat the pollen and nectar stored in the nest, although worker bees defend it with their stings. Some predators will also eat the larvae, pupae, or even the adult bees, often dormant overwintering queens.

These predators include mice, shrews, voles, weasels, badgers, foxes, birds, moths, spiders, and mites. Bumblebees are also attacked by parasitic wasps and flies which lay their eggs inside the bee. The parasite's eggs hatch into grubs and slowly eat their victim alive from the inside out.

Other population regulators include parasites and pathogens that live inside the bee, such as viruses, bacteria, protozoa (single-celled organisms) and tiny worms called nematodes. Bumblebees are also at risk from new parasites that may be carried into the country by commercially-reared bumblebee colonies.

These colonies are used for pollinating crops such as tomatoes grown in greenhouses. However, they might pose a threat to wild bees if they are not screened for diseases.

Opposite Left: Monoculture of wheat with no wild flowers at all
Opposite Bottom: Fox
Top: Farm with wild flower meadow
Above: Badgers

One of the best plants you can grow for bumblebees is Lavender. Choose a cultivar of English Lavender and your garden will have bumblebee visitors all summer.

Bees find it much easier to collect pollen and nectar from simple, open-faced flowers like dog roses. The flower sits, like a dinner plate, inviting the bee to collect food.

Try to include some plants which flower later in the year like Sedum (left) Honeysuckle, Comfrey and Sunflower. By having a range of plants throughout the seasons you will provide food for the whole bumblebee lifecycle.

Bees enjoy composite flowers such as alliums (right). The fact that each head is made up of hundreds of tiny flowers means the bee can move easily from flower to flower without wasting energy in flight.

Bumblebees enjoy Borage as much as Lavender and this plant will self-seed all over the garden, providing forage in spring and summer.

Planting a range of flower shapes will cater for the differing tongue lengths of bumblebees. Long-tongues will enjoy tubular flowers such as foxgloves, penstemons (right) and verbenas.

Creating new habitat for bumblebees

Gardens are really important for bumblebees and can provide fantastic nesting and foraging habitat. In a landscape that has experienced huge losses and a break-up of natural environments, gardens can provide vital links between wild spaces. They can contribute to green corridors and provide a mix of habitats, creating a more connected network of wildlife-friendly areas.

The key to a bumblebee-friendly garden is having the right plants at the right time, providing a steady supply of pollen and nectar throughout the bumblebee lifecycle, which lasts from March to October. No matter what size of garden or what type of soil you have, there are lots of options for turning your outside space into a bumblebee-friendly area.

WINDOW BOXES, POTS AND CONTAINERS

Containers, pots and window boxes can provide a feast for bumblebees across the seasons. Plant up pots with Crocus bulbs to provide an early meal. Sow with summer annuals, such as nasturtiums, (which can be trained up a trellis to save space), cornflowers, poppies, Borage, Cosmos and Phacelia.

Many herbs will tolerate the drier conditions of containers. Lavender, Rosemary, Oregano, chives, Mint, Lemon balm and Thyme, left to flower, are fantastic summer bumblebee food plants. All these plants will also do well planted in sunny areas of the garden.

GARDENING IN SHADY AREAS

Even damp, shady areas of the garden can provide good bumblebee food. Early flowering species including Lungwort, Hellebore, Comfrey, Primrose and Solomon's Seal and later flowering species including Bugle, hardy geraniums/cranesbills, Red Campion, Dog Rose, Honeysuckle, Foxglove and Wild Strawberry all provide good food sources. Ivy is a fantastic late forage and grows in the shadiest part of the garden with no help. Ivy is a great way to provide food for the last of the season's bumblebees.

TREES AND HEDGING PLANTS

Tree and hedging plants are a great addition to the garden bumblebee food options. Try Willow, Apple, Cherry, Plum, Pear and Blackthorn.

LAWNS

Even the humble lawn can be a food provider, with species often seen as 'weeds', such as clovers and dandelions, providing important food sources for bumblebees.

ALLOTMENTS

Many of our food plants are pollinated by bumblebees; allotments and vegetable gardens provide a huge variety of forage particularly in the summer. Bean and pea crops, courgettes, pumpkins and squashes, tomatoes and strawberries are all pollinated by bumblebees. Even brassicas, Broccoli and cauliflowers, onions and leeks, all provide great forage for bumblebees when the plants have 'gone over' and started to flower. Fruit bushes also provide a feast for us and the bumblebees! Blackberries, raspberries, currants and gooseberries are all favourites.

SUNNY SPOTS

Sunny areas of the garden can provide a huge variety of foraging opportunities. Early flowering species include Pieris, winter heathers, Flowering Current and Comfrey. Summer flowering species include Cat Mint, alliums, chives, sedums, Jacob's-ladder, knapweeds, Salvia, snapdragons, Scabious, Teasel, sweet peas, thistles, Vipers' Bugloss and sunflowers.

CREATING PONDS AND DAMP AREAS

Creating a pond is excellent for a whole range of wildlife. Yellow Flag Iris, Marsh Cinquefoil and Watercress are excellent forage for bumblebees within a pond. Around the outside you can add Water Mint, Purple Loosestrife, Forget-me-not, Marsh Marigold and Meadowsweet.

ENCOURAGING NESTING HABITAT

The best way to attract bumblebees to nest in your garden is by leaving some wild areas for nesting habitat; the back of borders, bases of hedgerows and grassy corners of the garden are all potential nesting sites. Undisturbed dry spots will encourage voles to make nests, which in turn provide nesting spaces for some bumblebee species. Other species are more opportunistic and may use compost heaps, bird boxes, or nest under sheds. Artificial housing is most frequently used by solitary bee species; mason bees and leaf cutters commonly use 'bee hotels' constructed from bamboo canes.

If you're lucky enough to find a bumblebee nest in your garden, leave it undisturbed; nests typically last around two to four months from start to finish before dying away.

Bumblebees are not aggressive, only females can sting and will only do so if they feel threatened. Watching the comings and goings of a nest from a distance is a fantastic way to get an insight into the lives of the colony and knowing your garden is providing a home to these charismatic species is a real treat.

ATTRACTING BUMBLEBEES

The two things to remember when planning a bee-friendly garden are *feeding* and *nesting*. By choosing a wide range of plants that flower through the year you can ensure that bees will have forage throughout their lifecycle. The next necessity for bees is somewhere to nest and, later, to hibernate.

Paving stones, sheds and rockeries often have redundant rodent nests beneath them and these sites are favoured by some bumblebees as nesting sites. Carder bees prefer long grass, so leave some areas unmown. Leaving piles of old logs, leaf litter, or creating a compost heap gives overwintering queens somewhere safe to hibernate.

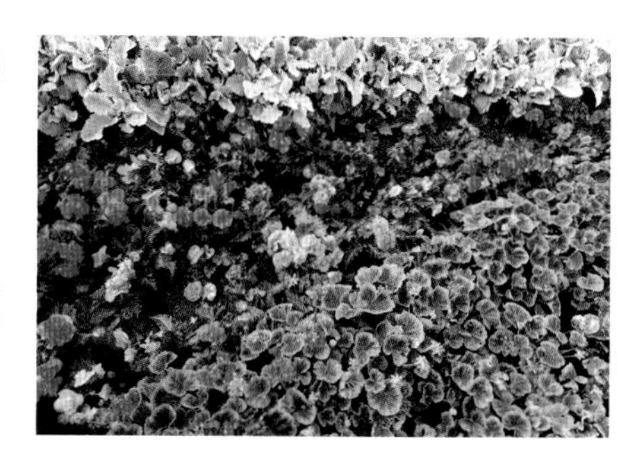

WHAT TO AVOID

Avoid traditional bedding plants such as petunias, begonias, and annual pelargoniums. These plants have been bred to be showy, colourful and long-lived but they contain little pollen and nectar and so are of little benefit to bees.

Many highly-cultivated flower varieties, including some roses and dahlias, have double blooms. This means there are lots of extra petals, laid out in a complicated pattern, which makes it difficult for bees to get to the pollen and nectar.

Avoiding herbicides and pesticides will be very beneficial to a range of wildlife in your garden and will help achieve the balance between garden pests and predators.

How to make a wildflower bed

First of all, cut your grass very short, rake off and remove all the cuttings. Make sure you take away the cuttings because leaving them on the ground can result in a high nutrient level, which is what you want to avoid. Wild flowers may fail if the soil is too rich so clear away all traces of grass cuttings.

Next, dig and hoe, or rotavate your area to expose the soil surface. It's important to create a fairly fine tilth or 'soil crumb' so that your seeds stand the best chance of germinating. The finer the tilth you create, the more chance your flowers have of getting off to a good start.

Sow your seeds, by hand, directly onto the soil surface. Do not cover the seeds with soil as they need to be on the soil surface to germinate. Wildflowers are not like garden flowers and do not need to be sown in furrows or planted under the soil.

Lightly tread or roll the seeds in and water well. The best time to sow wild flower seeds directly onto the soil is mid-July to mid-September, if your soil is not clay, you can sow in spring. Another choice is to plant seeds into a tray and then plant out as seedlings: this will increase their chances of establishing well.

Dig up or pull thistles, docks and nettles as they start to grow because they can take over and swamp the wild flowers. To extend the growing season cut some of the area in mid-July and remove all the cuttings as this dead-heads the flower. They will then flower again and continue until the end of August or September.

Do leave some areas uncut for forage for the bees. Cut again once the area has set seed. Leave the cuttings to dry for a few days before removing them, this will allow seeds to drop into the soil. Finally rake off and remove all cuttings.

Yellow Rattle is great for introducing into a wild flower bed. It partially parasitises grasses, reducing their coverage and opens up space for other wild flowers to succeed. Sow seeds in the autumn: they need a prolonged chilling to break the dormancy of their seeds.

Even very young children will enjoy spotting bees and trying to identify them. A simple fold-out identification guide can be carried in a pocket for easy reference.

Very little kit is needed to make surveying easier. A net, a 'queen plunger', specimen pot, magnifying glass and notebook will give you everything you need. If you have a camera or phone, taking photos in the field can help with identification later.

Children are always fascinated by the chance to look at bees close up. A large specimen pot, or a pot with a built-in magnifier attached to one end, gives kids a really good view.

Try setting up a bumblebee survey route, called a 'BeeWalk', in your area. The scheme runs throughout the UK and helps us understand more about bumblebee increases and declines.

Attending a bee identification course is a great way to make a start with working out which bee is which. Expert guidance is always useful to help you on your way to finding and recording bumblebees in the field.

Once you have a bee in your net, carefully potting it makes it so much easier to look at and identify.

Collecting information

One of the most important things we can do to help bumblebees is record our sightings of them. This shows what species are where and how many species are in different places.

This valuable information forms a window on the changing world of wildlife. It helps clarify which species are doing well, which are declining and where these declines are happening. It also shows how these changes may have been brought about by habitat, land-use or conservation work.

Records can be as simple as bee sightings that you have made in your garden, or on your way to work, or

they can evolve into more organised fixed-route recordings through BeeWalk: all records are valuable.

The Bees, Wasps and Ants Recording Society (BWARS), will be pleased to have the records and you can send all your sightings to them at www.brc.ac.uk/irecord.

The vast majority of what we currently know about where to find British bumblebees comes from records like this, combined with the hard work of BWARS down the years.

Left: If you pass some flowerbeds, you can count bees on a walk to work
Above: Even in the middle of the town, suitable beds will have bumblebees visiting

If you have some spare time every month in the spring and summer, the Bumblebee Conservation Trust runs a more in-depth recording scheme called BeeWalk. The idea of the BeeWalk is that volunteers walk along a set route, known as a 'transect', at least once a month between March and October, counting the number of individuals of each bumblebee species that they see. This produces useful information on abundance as well as distribution, and allows for a more detailed comparison between years. The transect can be any length, but the Bumblebee Conservation Trust generally recommends about a mile. It's not essential that the transect is constantly covered in flowers, but the more bumblebee-friendly plants you walk by, the more bees you'll see. If you'd like to join in visit: www.beewalk.org.uk.

Above: Investing in a net makes bee identification much easier
Right: A simple notebook makes recording more reliable. You can lose track of numbers easily while surveying

Equipment to make recording easier

At the simplest level, you can survey for bumblebees just by looking at bees sitting on flowers. Pretty soon though, you'll become annoyed by the bees flying off just as you're checking their identifying features.

Simple pieces of equipment such as a net and pot soon become 'must-haves' and will make your life so much easier. When choosing a net, make sure you get one with a fine mesh (no seaside shrimping-nets!), but beyond that any size or shape can be used. Once your bee is in the net, you'll need a clear, lidded pot such as a jam jar or specimen tube to put it in. Now you'll be able to have a really good look at it in order to see the smaller features for identification. Beekeepers have invented a handy device called a 'queen marking pot'

Left: Once you have the bee in your net it will nearly always crawl upward. Holding the net with the opening facing down means you won't lose your bee so easily
Above: The queen plunger allows lots of air in to keep the bee cool and gives you a good view

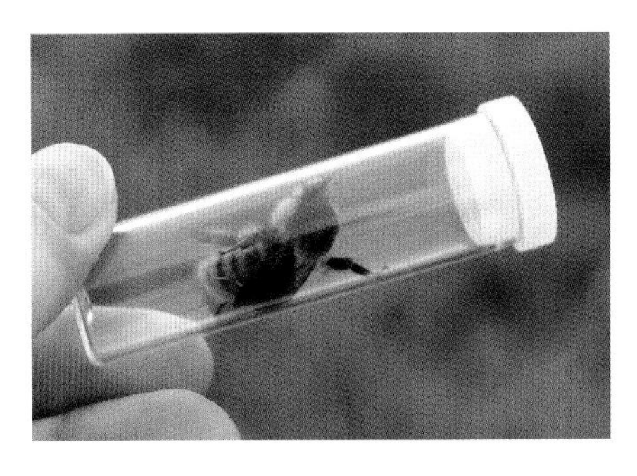

or 'queen plunger', which is useful for this. Basically it's a clear pot with an open mesh at one end and the lid replaced by a sponge-tipped plunger. This allows you to gently press the bee against the end of the pot, making it much easier to see the smaller details! It doesn't harm the bee as long as you are gentle. You shoudn't keep the bee in a pot for more than a few minutes, especially in full sun, because it will overheat and become stressed. Always release the bee back where you found it so that she can make it back to her nest. If you want to photograph your bees, they'll be less active when its cooler, so early mornings and late evenings can be good. Alternatively, popping the bee into a fridge or coolbox for a few minutes (only a few!) won't harm it and will slow it down enough to take pictures, particularly useful if you want to take close-ups.

Top Left: A clear specimen pot will give you a good view of your bee
Left: Even without a net or pot you can snap lots of photos of your bee and try to identify it later
Above: A small kit bag can hold everything you need

Buff-tailed bumblebee queen p72

Common carder bee queen p120

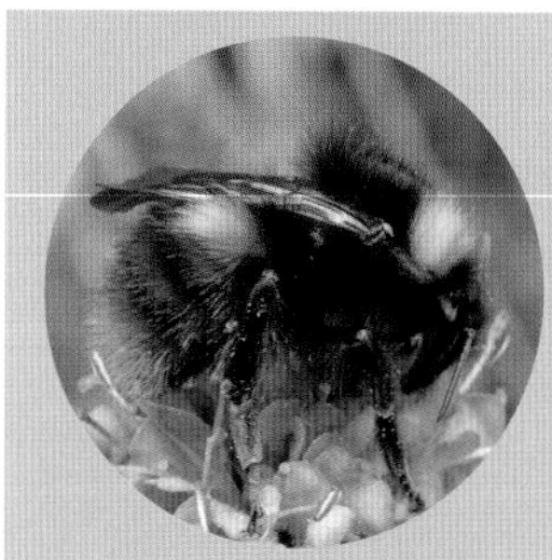

Red-tailed bumblebee queen p104

White-tailed bumblebee queen p84

Early bumblebee queen p112

Tree bumblebee queen p88

Garden bumblebee queen p76

The ‘Big Seven’

Of the UK’s twenty-four bumblebee species, seven are widespread, abundant and easy to see all over lowland Britain. We call these species the ‘Big Seven’ because these are the seven bees that you are most likely to find when you start ‘bee-spotting’.

THE ‘BIG SEVEN’ includes the Buff-tailed bumblebee, White-tailed bumblebee, Common carder bee, Garden bumblebee, Red-tailed bumblebee, Early bumblebee and a new addition to the UK, the Tree bumblebee. These species can be found in gardens across the UK. The Tree bumblebee has not yet reached parts of northern Scotland. If you live in the north you may find the Heath bumblebee very common.

LESS COMMON SPECIES

These bumblebees tend to be more localised and have a limited distribution across the UK. They include the Bilberry bumblebee, Broken-belted bumblebee and the Heath bumblebee. They may be quite plentiful in the areas where they are found.

CUCKOO SPECIES

Cuckoo bees are named after the bird because, just like their namesake, cuckoo species will parasitise their hosts’ nests. Once established in the hosts’ nest, the cuckoo will let the hosts’ own workers rear their offspring. There are six cuckoo species in the UK, the Southern cuckoo bee, Forest cuckoo bee, Barbut’s cuckoo bee, Gypsy cuckoo bee, Red-tailed cuckoo bee and Field cuckoo bee.

RARE SPECIES

These species are the UK’s most threatened. Some of them have declined by between 60-90% within their range, making them of grave concern in terms of conservation. These species include four Carder bees, the Brown-banded carder bee, Moss carder bee, Shrill carder bee and Red-shanked carder bee. There are also the Great Yellow bumblebee and the Ruderal bumblebee. Included in this section is the extinct Short-haired bumblebee. Attempts are currently being made in Kent to reintroduce this bee.

Heath bumblebee queen p80

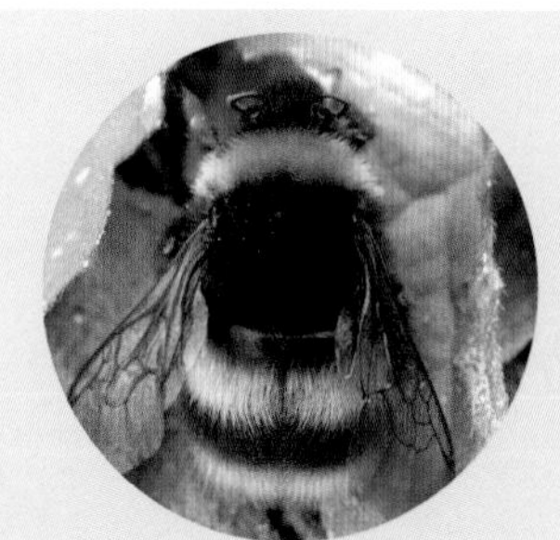

Broken-banded bumblebee queen p92

Bilberry bumblebee queen p116

Southern cuckoo bumblebee p140

Barbut's cuckoo bumblebee p160

Gypsy cuckoo bumblebee p148

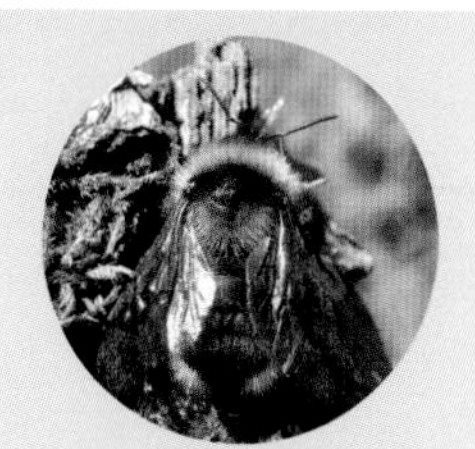

Field cuckoo bumblebee p144

Red-tailed cuckoo bumblebee p152

Forest cuckoo bee p156

Brown-banded carder bee p128

Moss carder bee queen p124

Ruderal bumblebee queen p96

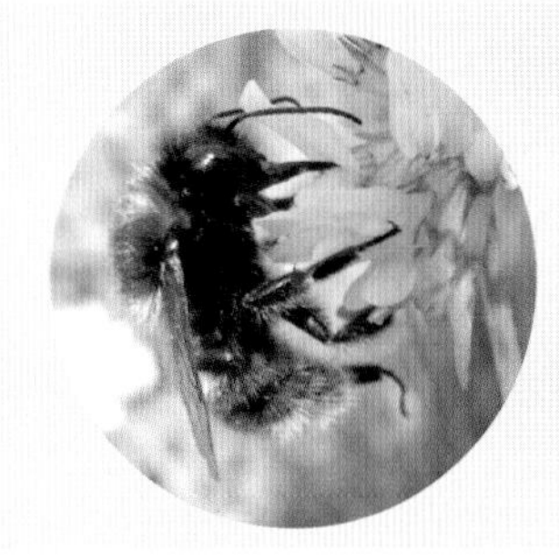

Red-shanked carder queen p108

Great Yellow bumblebee queen p136

Shrill carder bee queen p132

Short-haired bumblebee queen p100

This is an extinct bumblebee, currently undergoing reintroduction

CHAPTER 7

Bumblebee identification

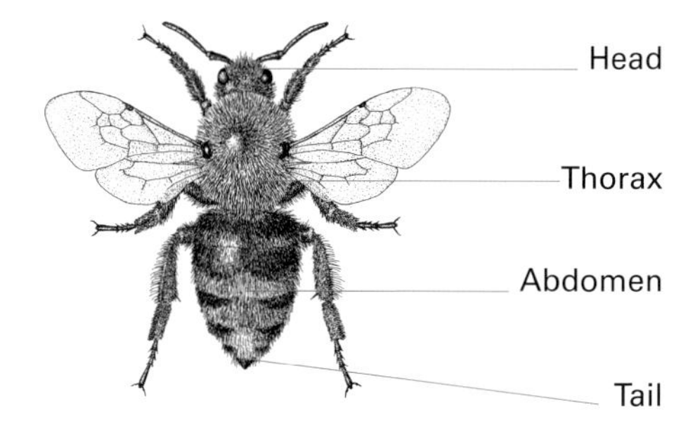

Five steps to identification

When you start identifying bumblebees you might find it a little daunting. Many species do appear to look similar but, if you follow the steps outlined here, look carefully at all the body features described and check with the identification pages, you should be able to work out which bumblebee you have. Practice is the key to identification. The more bumblebees you look at the easier you will find it to tell them apart.

First, catch your bee

The best way to identify a bumblebee is to net it and put it into a transparent pot so you can look closely at the features. You can keep the bumblebee still by placing some tissue into the pot before the bee goes in. If you put the tissue in the bottom of the pot the bee will stay at the top and you won't prevent it from flying off when it's time to let it go. Once netted, the bumblebee will usually crawl upwards, so keep the opening of the net towards the ground. Reach inside the net with the pot and encourage the bee into the opening. Put the lid on while the pot is still in the net to stop the bee escaping. Only keep the bee in the pot for a few minutes and make sure the pot has air holes to stop the bee overheating.

Step One: Look at the tail colour

The tail colour is the best place to start identification. In this book we divide bumblebees into white, red, ginger and yellow tails.

The first stage in identification is to focus on the tail colour

White tails
p72 -103

White-tailed cuckoo bees
p140, 148, 156 and 160

Ginger tails
p 120-135

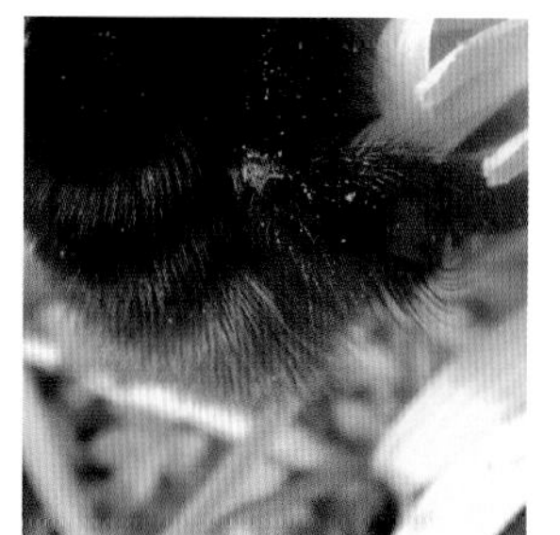

Red tails
p104-119

Red-tailed cuckoo bees
p152-154

Yellow tails
p136-139

Yellow-tailed cuckoo bee
p144-147

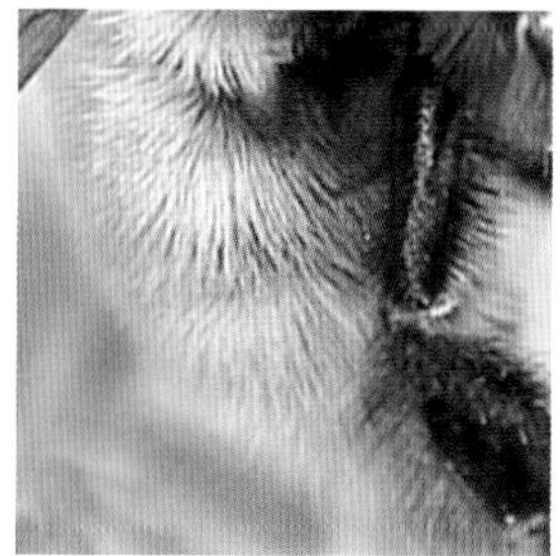

Step Two: Look at the banding on the thorax

Next look at the colour banding on the thorax. Many species may have a single yellow band at the top of the thorax like the White-tailed or Buff-tailed. Some species, such as the Garden bumblebee, have two yellow bands on the thorax on the top and bottom. Other species have just one colour on their thorax such as the Red-tailed (black) or Tree bumblebee (brown).

One thoracic band p72, 84, 92, 112

Cuckoo bees p140, 144, 148, 156

Two thoracic bands, p76, 80, 96, 100, 116, 132, 136, 144, 148, Males p104,108 Workers p144, 150, 160

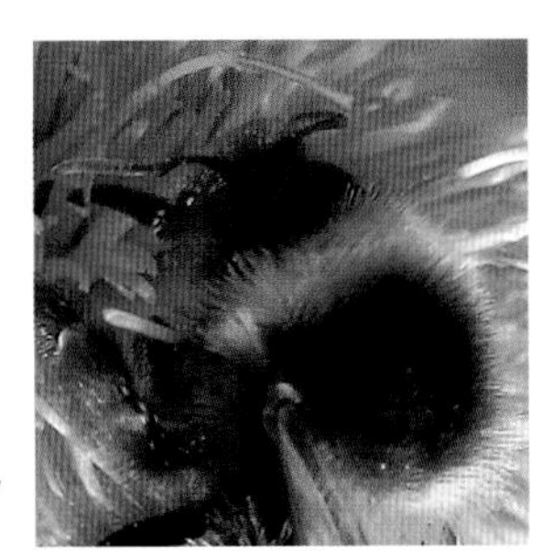

All ginger thorax p120, 124, 128

All black thorax p104, 108

Cuckoo bees p152

Two dull straw thoracic bands p134

All brown thorax p88

Stage two is to focus on the thorax banding or its solid colour

Stage three is to focus on the abdomen banding or its solid colour

Step Three: Look at the banding on the abdomen

Now look at the colour of the abdomen and check whether there are any abdominal bands. Some species, like the Early, Buff-tailed, Garden and White-tailed bumblebees, have a single yellow band. Others simply have a solid colour on the abdomen, such as the Red-tail, which is all black (until the tail).

One yellow abdominal band p72, 76, 80, 92, 96, 112

One brown band p128

All ginger abdomen p120, 124

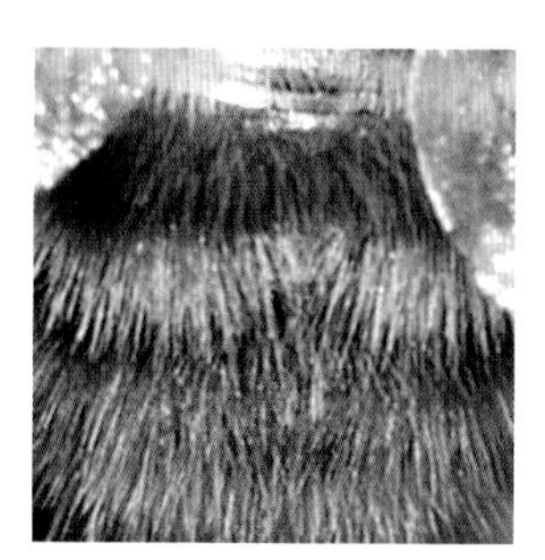

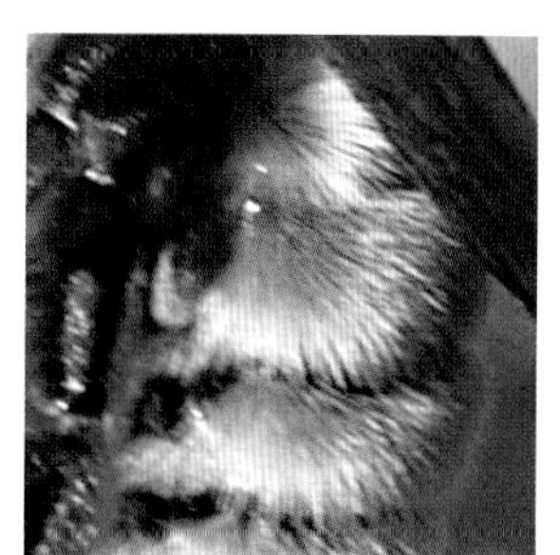

All yellow abdomen p136

All black abdomen p90, 104, 116,

Cuckoos p140, 144, 148, 152, 156

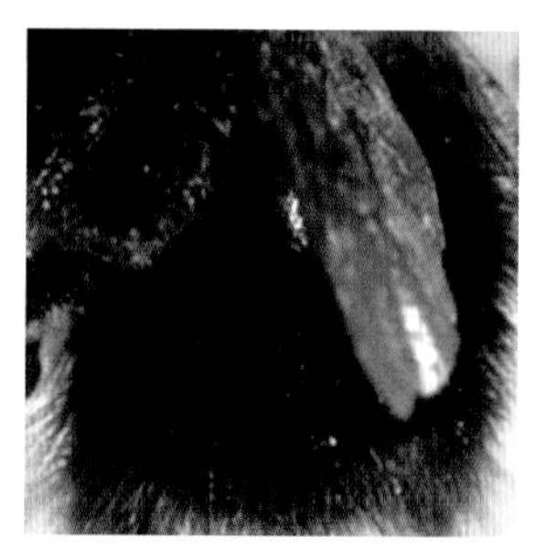

Step Four: Look at the shape of the hind legs

To determine whether your bumblebee is a male, female, or a cuckoo, look at the hind legs. You may need a hand lens to do this. All 'true' social bumblebee females have a pollen basket. If you see a ball of pollen on the hind leg, you have a female. Females also have long brush hairs on the hind leg that are used to help comb the pollen into a ball.

Males do not collect pollen but are often seen dusted in pollen all over their bodies. They have a hairy tibia and short stubble hair on the basitarsus - see illustration below.

Cuckoo bumblebees, whether male or female, do not collect pollen, however the cuckoo female does show a remnant of a pollen basket but no longer has the brush hairs. Male cuckoos have long hair on both their tibia and basitarsus - see illustration below.

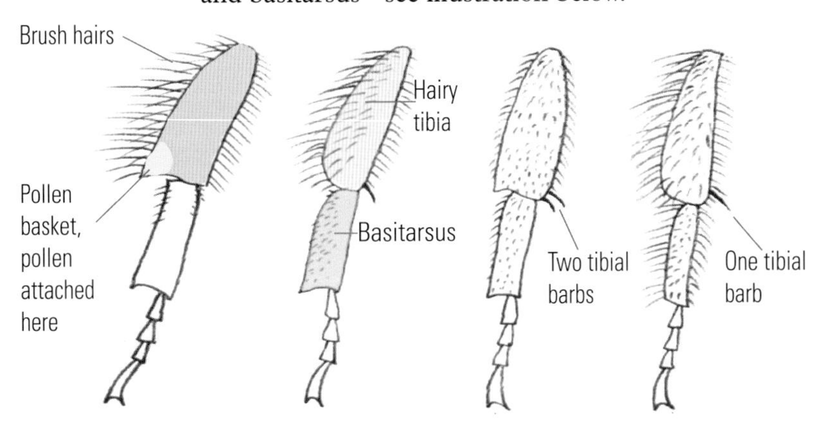

'True' female leg; long brush hairs on tibia and a pollen basket

'True' male leg; short hairy tibia and stubble hair on basitarsus

Cuckoo female leg; no brush hairs and no pollen basket

Cuckoo male leg; long hairs on both tibia and basitarsus

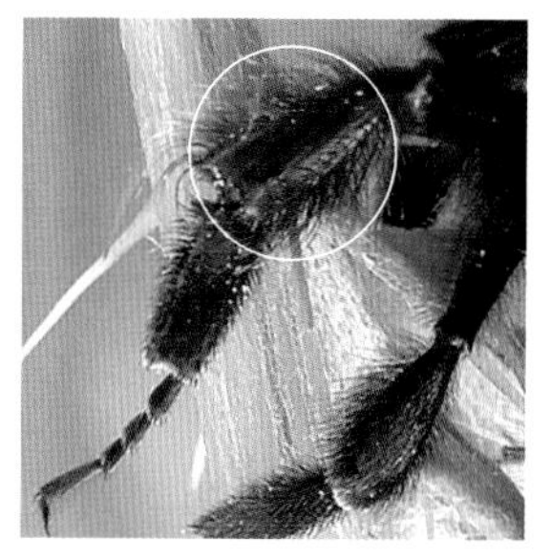

Female leg with flat, shiny pollen basket

'True' social male leg with hairy tibia and stubbly basitarsus

Cuckoo leg with barb

Stage four is to look at the hind leg

Stage five is to check the face shape

Step Five: Look at the shape of the face

To confirm your identification you can look at the face shape, although it is usually possible to confirm an identification without doing this. If you think you have found a Garden bumblebee, for example, look at the face to see if it is long and thin. Most other bumblebee species have a short face in comparison. All cuckoo bumblebees have a square head.

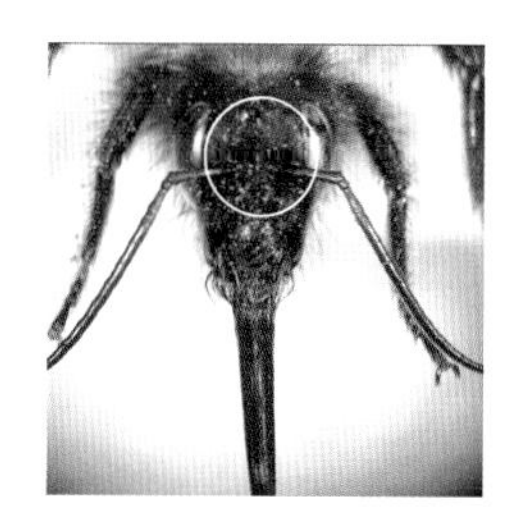

Long face

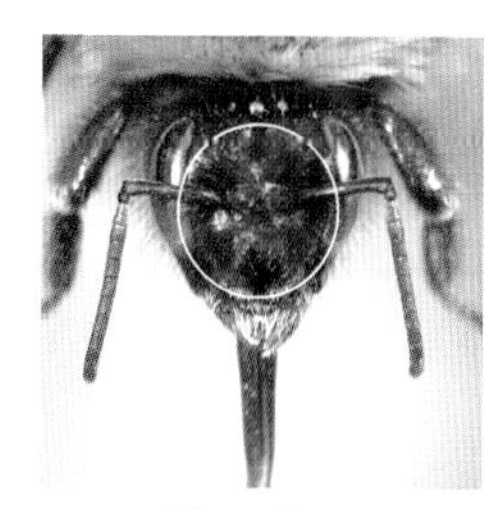

Short face

Cuckoo 'boxy' head

The Buff-tailed bumblebee *Bombus terrestris*

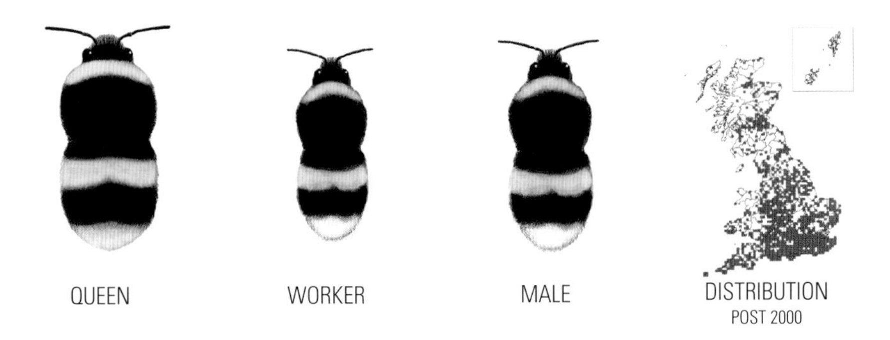

Where to find the Buff-tailed bumblebee

This is one of the Big Seven. The Buff-tailed bumblebee is one of the most common and widespread bumblebees in the UK. *Habitat:* Found in most habitats apart from high uplands.

When the queens emerge

The Buff-tailed bumblebee is one of the first species to emerge from hibernation in February. However in southern parts of England they may have a winter brood cycle and can be found nesting between October and March.

Where they nest

They nest underground in old rodent nests.

Their lifecycle

The nest lasts for 3-4 months. One or two generations a year, sometimes with another overwintering nest, particularly in Southern England.

Tongue length and flowers visited

They have a short tongue and forage on Willow, White Clover, heathers, Cotoneaster, Ivy and a wide variety of garden plants.

Q JAN FEB MAR APR MAY JUN JUL AUG SEP OCT NOV DEC
W
M

1. Remember there is only one broad dark yellow band on the thorax and one on the abdomen
2. There are buff orange hairs throughout the tail
3. Look for pollen baskets
4. These queens are the largest in the UK
5. Males and some workers have a line of yellow orange hair above the white tail
6. Males *never* have pollen baskets

Found in gardens

How to recognise queens, workers and males

THORAX Yellow-orange band at the top of the thorax and then black.
ABDOMEN One yellow-orange band near the top of the abdomen.
TAIL Queens have a buff/orange tail. Workers and males have a white tail, often with a thin line of orange hairs at the top. In males the orange line is more obvious than in workers.

What other species look similar?

White-tailed bumblebee Always has a pure-white tail, compared to the buff-orange of Buff-tailed queens. Buff-tailed and White-tailed workers are very similar, but workers of the former often have a thin line of orange hairs at the top of the white tail never present in the latter. Workers can be very difficult to separate in the field and, if unsure, should be recorded as 'worker Buff-tailed/White-tailed bumblebee'. The banding on the White-tailed is a bright lemon-yellow and male White-tailed have yellow facial hair.
Early bumblebee Similar yellow banding but has a red tail and is approximately half the size.
Broken-belted bumblebee Smaller and has a slightly longer face. The abdominal yellow bands come forwards onto the first segment of the abdomen at the sides. Male Broken-belted are fluffier than Buff-tailed males and have a peachy band of hair over the white tail.

Cuckoo

The Southern cuckoo bee uses the Buff-tailed bumblebee as a host.

The Early bumblebee (above) can cause mix ups, but it always has a red tail

Southern cuckoo bees mimic Buff-tails, but have visible chitin on the thorax and abdomen and short hair

White-tailed males (above) can cause confusion but they have a yellow, not a black, face

A queen Buff-tail (above) showing her characteristic buff-orange tail

A worker Buff-tail (above) has a much whiter tail with a line of orange hairs

This image, shot in winter, shows that the thick coat of a Buff-tailed bumblebee enables foraging in low temperatures

Buff-tails are found on many plants, including Lavender, Rose and marigolds

The Garden bumblebee *Bombus hortorum*

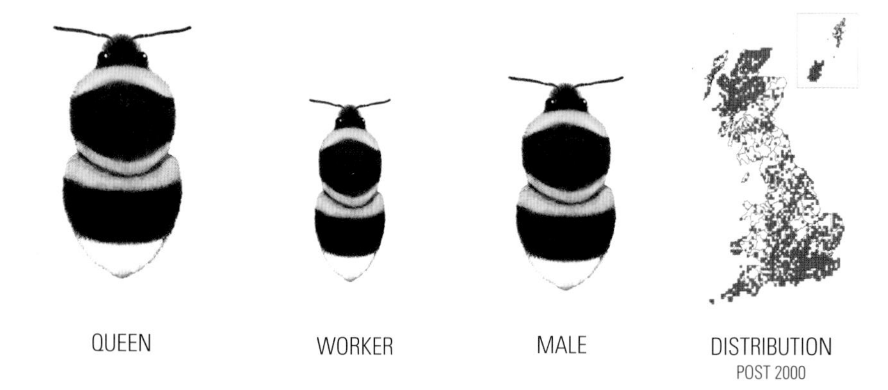

Where to find the Garden bumblebee

This is one of the Big Seven. Common and widespread throughout the UK. *Habitat;* present in most habitats and are commonly seen in gardens.

When the queens emerge

April onwards.

Where they nest

Mainly in old rodent nests.

Their lifecycle

The nest lasts for 3-4 months and contains up to 150 workers. In the southern parts of the UK Garden bumblebees will have a second cycle and continue until October.

Tongue length and flowers visited

Very long tongues (they are the longest in the world!) and like flowers such as Comfrey, bluebells, foxgloves, vetches, Red Clover and bird's-foot trefoils.

Q JAN FEB MAR APR MAY JUN JUL AUG SEP OCT NOV DEC
W
M

1. Remember that males, queens and workers all have the same colour pattern.
2. Two yellow bands; at front and back of thorax
3. There is always a third yellow band on the abdomen
4. Favourite forage: Comfrey, knapweeds, foxgloves
5. The banding is a lemon yellow colour
6. They have a long thin face with a very long tongue
7. The second thoracic band is narrower in width than the front band

How to recognise queens, workers and males

THORAX Two lemon yellow bands at the top and bottom of the thorax. The second band is narrower than the first. This bumblebee can also have a melanistic (dark) form, in which the yellow bands will turn black.

ABDOMEN Yellow band at the top of the abdomen and then black. In the melanistic form there is no yellow band.

TAIL White (even in melanistic individuals).

What other species look similar?

Heath bumblebee Very similar colour markings but have much shorter faces and are generally a much smaller species. Male Heath bumblebees have yellow facial hair.

Ruderal bumblebee Very similar banding but has shorter, 'cropped' hair, unlike the shaggy hair of the Garden bumblebee. A key difference is that the second thoracic band of the Ruderal is always the same depth as the front band. Both species produce melanistic (dark) individuals; the tail is black in the Ruderal but remains white in the Garden.

Cuckoo

The Barbut's cuckoo bee will use Garden bumblebee nests.

Buff-tails (left) can easily be confused with Garden bumblebees, but Buff-tails only have two yellow bands, Garden bumblebees have a second thoracic band as well as a band on the abdomen

Heath bumblebees (left) can cause confusion but they have a very much shorter, 'chubbier' face and longer hair

This female Barbut's cuckoo bee does its best to mimic a Garden bumblebee.
When making an identification, always look at the back legs. Cuckoos won't have pollen baskets

There is no upper abdominal yellow band as there is with the Garden.

The chitin on the exoskeleton is visible, where the Garden bumblebee has long, shaggy hair

Male Garden bumblebees (left) always have a long, black face

Long-tongued bees, like the Garden bumblebee (left), enjoy Borage, English Lavender, Comfrey, foxgloves and lots of other garden flowers. Many bumblebees especially benefit from the Bowle's Mauve form of Wallflower (left) which has a long flowering season

The Heath bumblebee *Bombus jonellus*

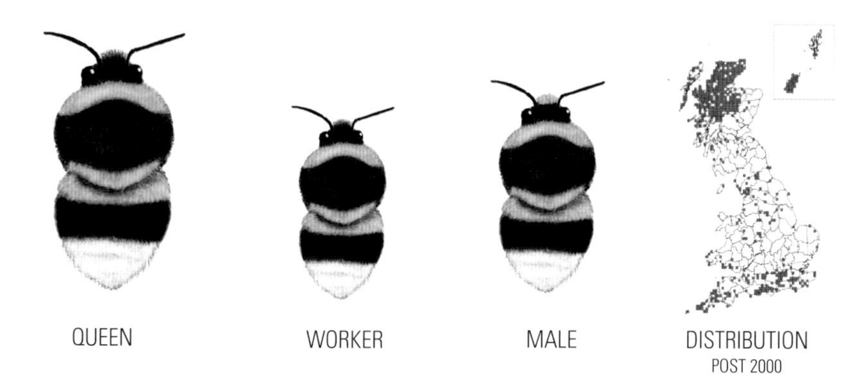

Where to find the Heath bumblebee

One of the less common bumblebees

The Heath bumblebee is found in uplands and acidic areas such as the highlands of Scotland, but is also found along the south coast of England, with scattered records elsewhere. *Habitat:* Heather-rich areas, gardens and parks.

When the queens emerge

From February onwards.

Where they nest

Mainly in old rodent nests, leaf litter on the surface of the ground and even old birds' nests.

Their lifecycle

Nests are small with up to 50 workers. One colony per year but two in the south of England.

Tongue length and flowers visited

This species has a short tongue and will forage on flowers such as Knapweed, heathers, ragworts and Red Clover.

Q JAN FEB MAR APR MAY JUN JUL AUG SEP OCT NOV DEC

W

M

1. This is a small to medium-sized bee
2. Three yellow bands: at top and bottom of thorax and on the abdomen
3. Don't confuse the lower thorax and upper abdomen bands as one wide band
4. Males and females have the same colouring
5. The Heath bumblebee has a short, wide face unlike the Garden bumblebee which is long and thin
6. Males of the Heath bumblebee have a yellow face where the Garden bumblebee male's face is black

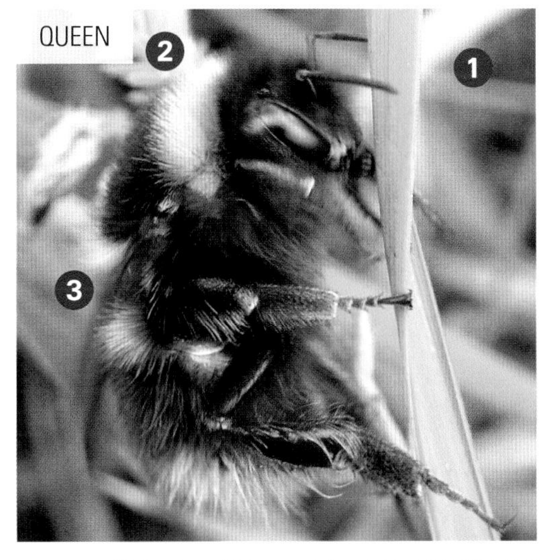

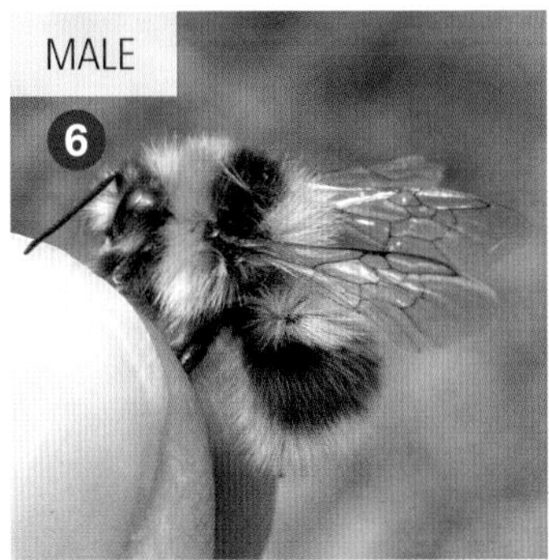

Found mainly on moorland and heathland

How to recognise queens, workers and males

THORAX Two yellow bands on the top and bottom with black in between.
ABDOMEN A yellow band at the top and black below.
TAIL White (or orange/buff in Shetland or the Western Isles).

What other species look similar?

Garden bumblebee Similar colouring to the Heath but the Garden has a very long face and tongue. The males of the Garden also have black hairs on the face whereas the Heath has yellow.
Ruderal bumblebee As with the Garden, similar colouring to the Heath but has a much longer face and tongue. The hair of the Ruderal is 'cropped' and shorter than the Heath. The males of the Ruderal also have black hairs on the face whereas the Heath has yellow.
White-tailed bumblebee Males look similar to the Heath and can have two yellow bands on the thorax like the Heath. The Heath is, however, a smaller bee with a rounder face.
Barbut's cuckoo bee Similar banding and face length to Heath, but darker wing membranes, sparser hair and hairier hind legs (especially noticeable in females).

Cuckoo

The Forest cuckoo bee will use the Heath bumblebee as a host.

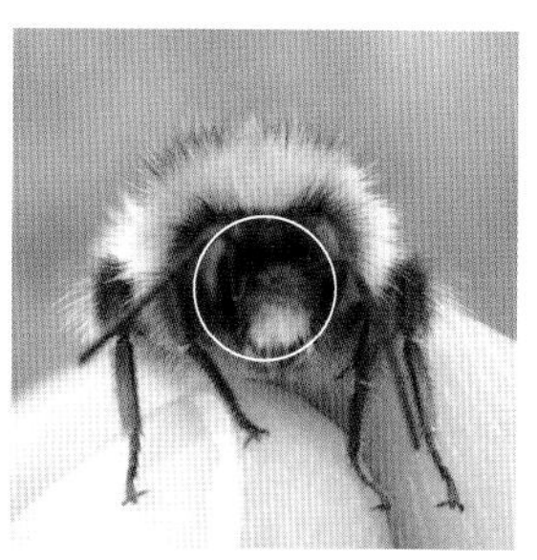

Heath bumblebees can be confused with Garden bumblebees. The Heath bumblebee (left) is generally smaller and has a much shorter, 'chubbier' face

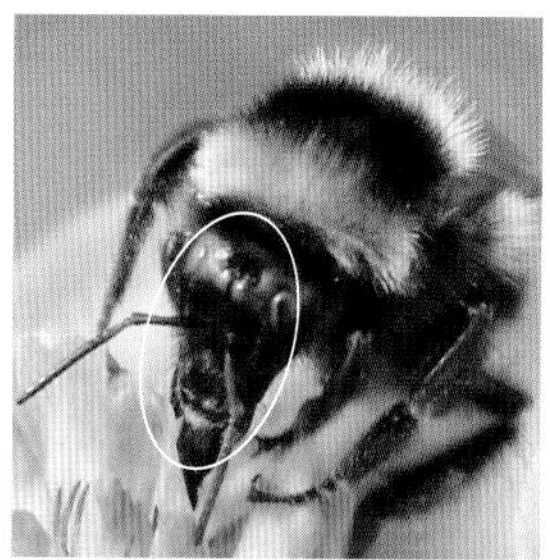

Garden bumblebees (left) can be confused with Heath bumblebees but they are usually bigger and they always have a very long, black face

Heath bumblebees (above) are small to medium bumblebees with long hair. They have been described as looking 'fluffy' or 'shaggy'

Small worker Buff-tails (left) may be confused with Heath bumblebees, but Heath bumblebees have two bands on the thorax and one on the abdomen and the Buff-tails only have one thoracic band

The Forest cuckoo female (left) uses the Heath bumblebee as its host. The cuckoo female only has one thoracic band. As with all cuckoos, her hair is sparse and the chitin can be seen through the hair

The Heath bumblebee (above) has three bands. Two are on the thorax and a third is at the top of the abdomen. Look carefully as the abdominal and thoracic bands may appear to merge and look like one

As suggested by its name, the Heath bumblebee prefers to feed on heathland plants such as heathers, knapweeds and clovers. These are all plants suited to short-tongued species

The White-tailed bumblebee aggregate *Bombus lucorum* agg

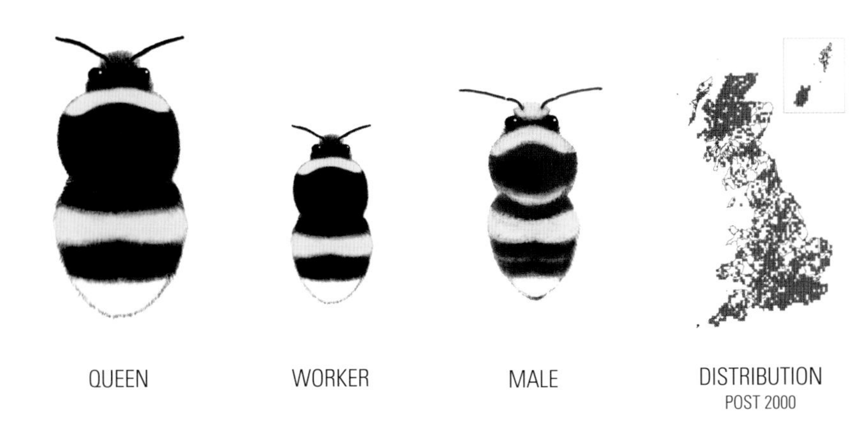

Where to find the White-tailed bumblebee

This is one of the Big Seven. This is an abundant species when taken as an aggregate. Identification difficulties make species-level distributions unreliable, but the White-tailed bumblebee appears to be a lowland species, with the Northern and Cryptic White-tailed bumblebees having more upland, northern and western distributions. Please see the box on page 85 for more details.
Habitat: Gardens and flowery meadows.

When the bees emerge

March - April.

Where they nest

Mainly in old rodent nests.

Their lifecycle

Nests are large, often around 200 workers and usually die off in August, although the species may have two generations per year in some areas or in warm summers.

Q W M JAN FEB MAR APR MAY JUN JUL AUG SEP OCT NOV DEC

1. The White-tailed bumblebee has a clean white tail with no orange-yellow hair above the white
2. The top collar band on White-tails is a much paler lemon-yellow than the Buff-tails' orange-yellow colour
3. Queens and workers have black hair on their faces
4. Males always have bright yellow hair on their faces

Found in gardens and flower-rich meadows

Tongue length and flowers visited

A short-tongued species, among other plants it forages on knapweeds, thistles and White Clover.

How to recognise queens and workers

THORAX Black with one yellow band at the top of the thorax.
ABDOMEN Black with one yellow band across the middle.
TAIL Bright, pure white.

How to recognise males

THORAX Black with one lemon yellow band at the top and one at the bottom of the thorax.
ABDOMEN Black with one lemon yellow band across the middle. White-tailed males can have several lemon-yellow bands on the abdomen, causing them to look very yellow all over.
TAIL Bright, pure white. FACE Lemon yellow.

What other species look similar?

Buff-tailed bumblebee Queens have a buff-yellow tail compared to the pure-white of the White-tail and this is easily seen. Buff-tailed bumblebee workers often have a thin line of orange-yellow above the tail which is absent in the White-tail. These workers can be difficult to separate in the field and, if you are unsure, they should be recorded as 'worker Buff-tailed/White-tailed bumblebee'. Male Buff-tail bumblebees have black facial hair compared to yellow on the male White-tail. All castes of the true White-tailed bumblebee are virtually indistinguishable from the Cryptic and Northern White-tailed bumblebees (see box opposite).

Cuckoo

The Gypsy cuckoo bee is thought to parasitise this species.

The obvious confusion is with the Buff-tail (left) but this bee does have an obviously buff-orange tail. Queens, workers and male Buff-tailed bumblebees have black faces

The Gypsy cuckoo bee (left) does its best to look like a White-tail. These males could be confused but the bands of the Gypsy are darker yellow and its chitin can be seen

White-tailed bumblebees (left) have short tongues. They forage on a range of plants including Viper's Bugloss (shown) clover and knapweeds that short-tongued bees enjoy

Male White-tailed bumblebees (above) have distinct, bright-yellow faces. They may also have several yellow bands on the abdomen, giving them a golden appearance. Males might be confused with the Great Yellow bumblebee but the latter is only found in a few places in Scotland so is an unlikely confusion in other parts of the UK

A recent discovery using DNA has shown that the bees which were once known as the White-tailed bumblebee are three separate species, the true White-tailed bumblebee, the Northern White-tailed bumblebee and the Cryptic bumblebee.

All castes of the true White-tailed bumblebee are virtually indistinguishable from equivalent castes of the Cryptic and Northern White-tailed bumblebee so identification is not possible without DNA testing. Currently scientists are looking into DNA and field identification techniques but at present all sightings should be recorded as 'White-tailed bumblebee aggregate'.

The Tree bumblebee *Bombus hypnorum*

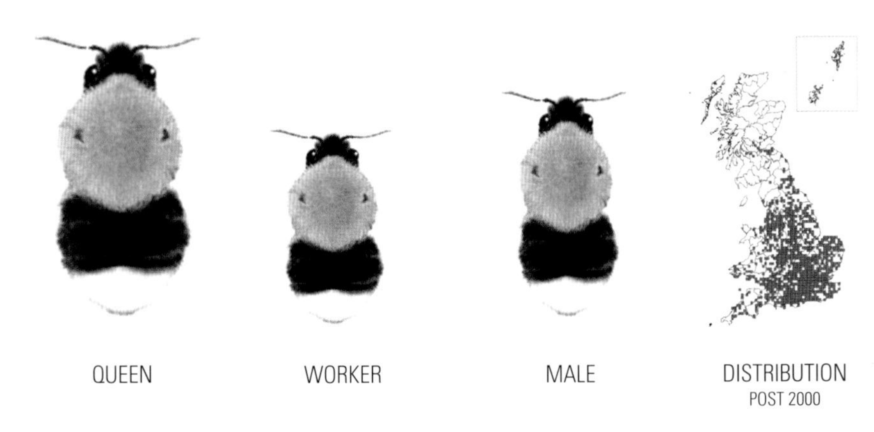

Where to find the Tree bumblebee

This is one of the Big Seven. These bees arrived in southern England in 2001 from mainland Europe. They have spread steadily and are now one of the UK's most common species. They are found all over England, much of Wales and are increasingly common in Scotland. *Habitat:* Found in most habitats, including suburbia.

When the queens emerge

February onwards.

Where they nest

Above ground in trees and will often make use of bird boxes and roof eaves.

Their lifecycle

The nest lasts for 2-3 months with up to 150 workers. They usually have two generations each summer. Males are often seen flying in large numbers (15-20) outside nest entrances during the summer months waiting for queens.

Q W M JAN FEB MAR APR MAY JUN JUL AUG SEP OCT NOV DEC

1. The thorax is a ginger brown
2. The abdomen is always black
3. The tail is always white
4. Workers will always have pollen baskets
5. The brown hair may extend onto the top of the abdomen and there can be melanistic forms where the brown hair is black but the tail remains white
6. Tree bumblebees are often found in bird boxes but may nest in odd places like an old tumble-drier

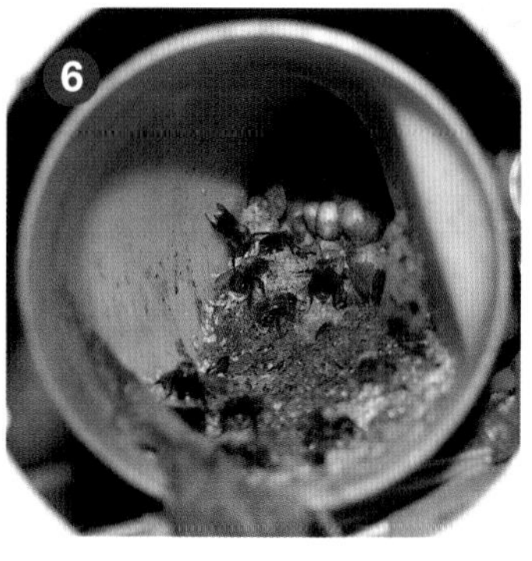

Found in gardens

Tongue length and flowers visited

A short-tongued species. They forage on flowers, including brambles, raspberries, open roses, Ceanothus and cotoneasters.

How to recognise queens, workers and males

THORAX Brown which can have black hair in varying amounts in melanistic individuals.
ABDOMEN The abdomen is black, occasionally with a brown band at the very front of the abdomen.
TAIL White.

What other species look similar?

Common carder bee Has an all-ginger abdomen with varying amounts of scattered black hairs, rather than the clear black band and white tail of the Tree bumblebee. It has pale beige thorax sides not present in the Tree Bumblebee.
Garden bumblebee also has a melanistic (black) form with a white tail but the face and tongue are much longer than those of the Tree bumblebee.

Cuckoo

This species has no known cuckoo bees in the UK.

Tree bumblebees are very distinctive. However you might mistake a Common carder bee (left) for one if you can't see the tail, which will be white in Tree bumblebees

Carder bees (left) have longer faces so you can use this as another method to stop confusion with the Tree bumblebee

Above you can see a typical example of confusion between Tree bumblebees and Common carder bees. The Tree bumblebee (on the left of the flower), will always have a bright white tail while the Common carder bee (on the right) has no white tail and usually has a stripier abdomen

Here, the queen Tree bumblebee has her tail tucked under, but you can see she is not a Common carder bee by the short, round face

Classic colouring on a Tree bumblebee, brown thorax, black abdomen and a bright white tail

On older bees, the thorax can fade and the white tail can become worn away (above), but the Tree bumblebee should still have a few distinctive white tail hairs so that you can make an identification

The Broken-belted bumblebee *Bombus soroeensis*

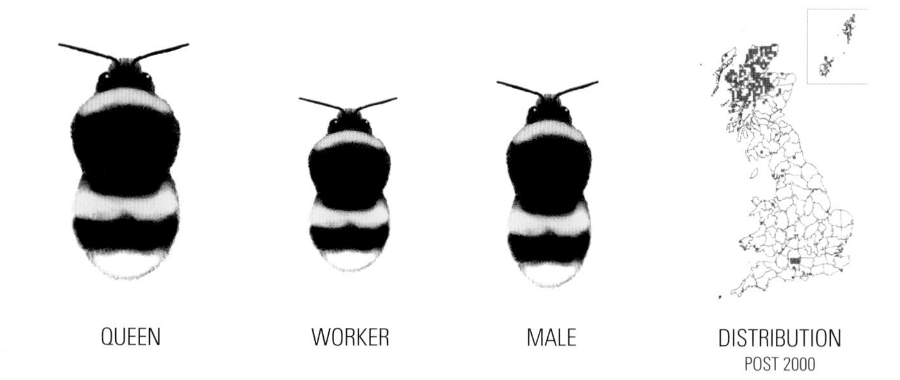

Where to find the Broken-belted bumblebee	*This is a less common species.* This bumblebee is found infrequently in England and Wales but is still frequent in the Scottish Highlands where it can be found at high altitudes. *Habitat:* Associated with moorlands but also found on heathlands and chalk grasslands.
When the queens emerge	May onwards.
Where they nest	Mainly in old rodent holes.
Their lifecycle	Their nests last for 2-4 months and normally contain between 80 - 150 workers. New males and queens can be seen from September onwards.
Tongue length and flowers visited	Tongue length: Short. This bee favours clovers, brambles, heathers, knapweeds and Scabious.

Q JAN FEB MAR APR MAY JUN JUL AUG SEP OCT NOV DEC
W
M

1. The single band on the thorax is a bright yellow

2. The yellow band on the abdomen often has a dark notch in the middle

3. Queens have a fringe of orange/buff hairs between the dark hairs of the abdomen and the white tail hairs

4. Workers have a lot of peach-coloured hair above the white tail

5. Males will sometimes have a peach band but this is not always visible

Found on moorland

How to recognise queens, workers and males

THORAX Bright yellow band at the top of the thorax and then black hairs.
ABDOMEN Bright yellow band top of the abdomen and then black hairs. The yellow abdominal band sweeps forward towards the thorax at the sides, and often has a black notch in the middle. Despite its common name the notch in the abdominal band is not the deciding factor in identification. Females have a fringe of orange/buff coloured hair above the tail, which is more noticeable in workers. TAIL White tail; males can have orange/buff tails.

What other species look similar?

White-tailed bumblebee Has a neater, more rectangular abdominal yellow band which does not cross onto the first abdominal section, even on the sides of the abdomen. Can be very difficult to distinguish without microscopic examination.
Early bumblebee The Early male has yellow facial hairs and a tail which is red-ginger throughout. Broken-belted males have dark facial hair and a peach-and-white tail.

Cuckoo

This species has no known cuckoo bees in the UK.

Confusion can easily take place between White-tailed and Broken-belted bumblebees but the White-tailed (left) is usually considerably larger

A Broken-belted bumblebee (left) shows the bright lemon yellow bands. The 'broken' abdominal band shows the central notch of black hairs and chitin is visible

The Broken-belted bumblebee favours moorland and high-altitude sites

A male Broken-belted bumblebee (below) showing bright yellow bands, an orange tail and a distinct gap in the yellow band

Male Broken-belted bumblebees (left) can be mistaken for Early males because they can have an orange tail, but in Broken-belted males the facial hair is always black

Found on moorland and uplands

The Ruderal bumblebee *Bombus ruderatus*

LIGHT FORM
QUEEN

INTERMEDIATE FORM
QUEEN

DARK FORM
QUEEN

DISTRIBUTION
POST 2000

Where to find the Ruderal bumblebee

This is a rare species. This bumblebee has declined significantly in the UK and is one of the UK's rarest bumblebees. It is still found in isolated locations in the south of England up to Lincolnshire, but is absent from Scotland. There are few recent records from Wales. *Habitat:* Wild flower meadows and agricultural 'pollen and nectar' mixes.

When the queens emerge

April onwards.

Where they nest

Mainly in old rodent holes.

Their lifecycle

Nests tend to be quite large with over 150 workers and just one colony per year of 3-4 months. New queens and males will appear from July onwards.

Tongue length and flowers visited

This very long-tongued bee will forage on Red Clover, White dead-nettle, Comfrey, foxgloves and vetches.

Q JAN FEB MAR APR MAY JUN JUL AUG SEP OCT NOV DEC
W
M

LIGHT FORM QUEEN

INTERMEDIATE FORM QUEEN

DARK FORM QUEEN

1. Note that the bands are darkish yellow with a thick band of black hair between. The bands are the same width at the top and bottom of the thorax

2. Yellow bands are darker with much more dark hair. The white tail is still present, but with much more black hair visible

3. The most obvious feature of the dark form is that it is black all over in the queen, worker and male

LIGHT FORM MALE

INTERMEDIATE FORM WORKER

DARK FORM MALE

4. Males will never have pollen baskets on the hind legs

5. The third band on the abdomen can be very hard to make out on an intermediate form

6. This is a big bee. Both males and females are extremely large. They can look bullet-shaped

Found on flower meadows

How to recognise queens, workers and males

LIGHT FORM

THORAX Two dark yellow bands on the thorax are the same depth as each other with a band of black hairs across the wing bases.

ABDOMEN Top of abdomen has yellow hairs, then black hairs throughout.

TAIL White.

INTERMEDIATE FORM

THORAX Same as the light form, but the bands are thinner.

ABDOMEN Black hairs throughout.

TAIL White but darkening with black hairs.

DARK FORM

THORAX All black.

ABDOMEN All black.

TAIL All black.

What other species look similar?

Garden bumblebee Has paler yellow bands than the Ruderal and on the thorax the rear band is narrower than the front (equal depth in Ruderal). In dark form individuals, the tail of the Garden bumblebee remains white (black in the Ruderal).

Heath bumblebee Has longer hair compared to the 'cropped' hair of the Ruderal and is also smaller with a much shorter face.

Short-haired bumblebee The bottom thoracic band is narrower than the top band (equal depth in Ruderal), and tends to have several thin yellow abdominal bands.

Cuckoo

This bumblebee is thought to be a host to Barbut's cuckoo bee.

Ruderal bumblebees have very long tongues and can feed on plants that are inaccessible to other bees. Note the band width on the thorax; both are the same thickness

This male Garden bumblebee (left) could easily be confused with a light form Ruderal, but the Garden bumblebee has a much thinner second thoracic band

Ruderal bumblebees enjoy *Acanthus spinosus*, known as Bears' Britches (above), because they provide a lot of pollen and nectar. They are one of the few bumblebees large enough to force the flower open to access the pollen and nectar. Note the long tongue

Barbut's cuckoo bee (left) can be mistaken easily for the light form of its host, the Ruderal bumblebee, however this bee always has a square 'boxy' head

Ruderal bumblebees have a very longue tongue and favour plants with trumpet-like flowers, such as vetches and clovers (right). Favourite habitat includes flower-rich meadows

The Short-haired bumblebee *Bombus subterraneus*

Where to find the Short-haired bumble bee

Prior to its extinction this bumblebee was commonly seen in the south east of England and was found as far north as Humberside in Yorkshire. However, its population started to decline dramatically during the 1960's and 1970's and it was last seen in the UK in 1988 in Kent. It was declared extinct in 2000. This bumblebee is currently part of a reintroduction project based in Kent and East Sussex run by Bumblebee Conservation Trust, RSPB and Natural England.
Habitat: Strongly associated with flower-rich meadows.

When the queens emerge

May onwards.

Where they nest

Mainly old rodent holes.

Their lifecycle

The colony will live for 3-4 months and have between 75-150 workers.

Q JAN FEB MAR APR MAY JUN JUL AUG SEP OCT NOV DEC
W
M

1. The face is long, but 'chubbier' than that of a Garden or Ruderal bumblebee

2. The hair is very, very short

3. There is always a bald spot on the thorax

4. The second thoracic band is much thinner

5. Queens and workers have the same colour pattern

6. Males can be easily distinguished trom temales because they are completely yellow with a single wide black thoracic band

Found in gardens and flower-rich meadows

Tongue length and flowers visited	They have a long tongue and like flowers such as Red Clover, White dead-nettle, bird's-foot trefoils and vetches.
How to recognise queens and workers	THORAX There are two yellow bands at the top and bottom of the thorax. The bottom band is always narrower in depth than the first. The top band will often have a black notch of hairs in the middle. ABDOMEN There are faint yellow/grey bands on the abdomen and often a faint yellow band above the tail. TAIL Often white, but can go chocolate-brown. The short hair on the thorax and abdomen means that the chitin is often visible.
How to recognise males	THORAX Two pale yellow bands on the top and bottom of the thorax with a band of black hair between the wing bases. ABDOMEN Yellow throughout but with some black hairs on the second segment. TAIL Yellow.
What other species look similar?	*Garden bumblebee* Has brighter yellow bands, a longer face and generally longer hair than the Short-haired. In melanistic (dark) individuals the tail colour will remain white (chocolate-black in the Short-haired). *Ruderal bumblebee* The top and bottom bands of the thorax are the same depth but the bottom band in the Short-haired is narrower.
Cuckoo	This bumblebee is thought to be a host to the Barbut's cuckoo bee.

Confusion might happen with the Garden Bumblebee (left) but this bee has much longer hair. Unless it is badly worn, it will not have a bald patch on the thorax

The Ruderal bumblebee (left) has a longer face than the Short-haired Bumblebee. It also has longer, hair and both thoracic bands are the same width

The Short-haired Bumblebee (below) shows the bald spot on the thorax. The second thoracic band is narrower than the top band. The hair is short like a 'crew-cut'

The Red-tailed bumblebee *Bombus lapidarius*

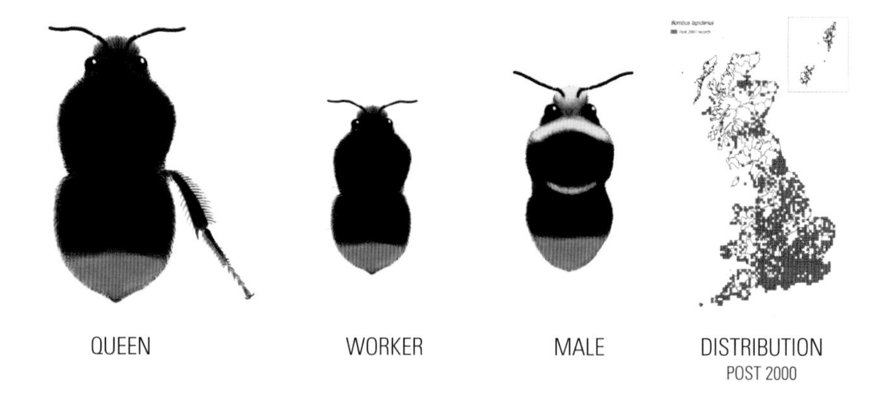

Where to find the Red-tailed bumblebee	*One of the Big Seven.* This bumblebee is common throughout the UK, becoming scarcer in northern Scotland. *Habitat:* Grassland, woodlands and gardens.
When the queens emerge	March onwards.
Where they nest	Underground or in enclosed locations.
Their lifecycle	The cycle lasts 3-4 months with up to 300 workers. New queens and males emerge from late June and can have two generations a year in the south.
Tongue length and flowers visited	Medium. The Red-tailed bumblebee favours dandelions, Lavender and Honeysuckle.
How to recognise queens and workers	THORAX Black. ABDOMEN Black. TAIL Red, fading to ginger. LEG HAIR Black.

Q JAN FEB MAR APR MAY JUN JUL AUG SEP OCT NOV DEC

M

1. Black velvety hairs on thorax and abdomen
2. Bright 'fire-extinguisher red' tail. This will fade to ginger
3. Note pollen baskets on the leg
4. Males have yellow facial hair
5. Males have two yellow bands on the thorax
6. Males have visibly longer hair

Found in gardens

How to recognise males

THORAX Black with two yellow bands at the top and bottom.
ABDOMEN Black.
TAIL Red, fading quickly to ginger then yellow.
HEAD Has yellow facial hairs.

What other species look similar?

Red-shanked carder bee Smaller, rounder and appear more fluffy than the Red-tailed. Queens and workers have obvious red hairs fringing the pollen baskets (black in the Red-tailed) and male Red-shanked carders have black facial hairs (yellow in the Red-tailed).
Red-tailed cuckoo bee Has an obviously 'square' head, very dark wings and sparse hair coverage giving a bald, shiny appearance. The male Red-tailed cuckoo also has black facial hair compared to the yellow of the Red-tailed male.
Early bumblebee Has yellow bands, one on the thorax and one other on the top of the abdomen. Male Red-tailed bumblebees have no abdominal yellow bands, and female Red-tailed have no yellow bands at all.

Cuckoo

The Red-tailed cuckoo bee uses the Red-tailed bumblebee as the host species.

This Red-tailed bumblebee worker shows its bright red tail. Its wings are clear, it carries pollen, and the tail has a straightish demarcation line confirming it is a 'true' Red-tailed worker

Confusion can occur with the Red-tailed cuckoo (left). One key is to look at the wings which, in the cuckoo, are always dark. The tail is an orangey colour rather than red

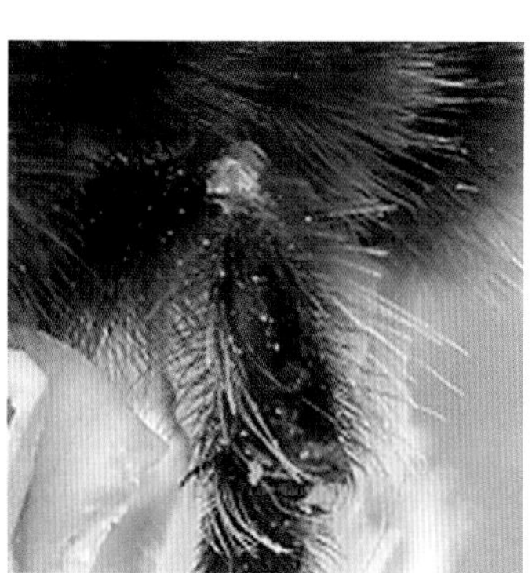

Confusion could also occur with the Red-shanked carder but this bee has distinctive orange leg hairs. It is also much rarer than the Red-tailed bumblebee

The Red-tailed bumblebee is very common and can easily be found on flowery grassland (top), woodland edges (middle) and flowery gardens (bottom)

The Red-tailed worker (left) has a characteristic bright-red tail and velvety black hair

The yellow hair on the Red-tailed male (left) has faded during the course of the year, but a faint orange-red tail is still visible

The Red-shanked carder bee *Bombus ruderarius*

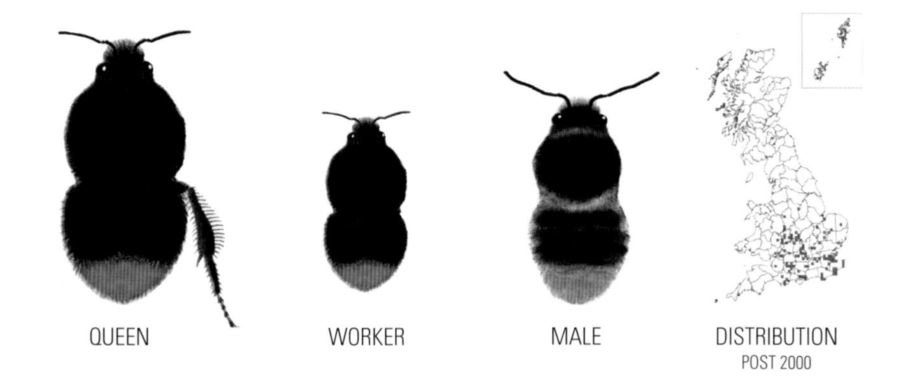

Where to find the Red-shanked carder bee	*This is a rare bumblebee.* This bee has suffered a large decrease over the last 30 years and is now one of the UK's rarest species. Found in isolated locations in south-east, south-west and central England, south Wales and the Inner Hebrides in Scotland. *Habitat:* Flower-rich grasslands.
When the queens emerge	April.
Where they nest	On the surface of the ground in long grass, although they can use disused rodent holes just below the ground surface. They use grass clippings and moss to form their nests.
Their lifecycle	Worker numbers range from 20-100. The colony will live for 3-4 months. New queens and males will appear from July onwards.

Q JAN FEB MAR APR MAY JUN JUL AUG SEP OCT NOV DEC
W
M

1. The most important feature to look for is the bright red hairs on the hind legs
2. The tail colour is more orangey than red
3. Workers share the same bright red leg hairs as the queens
4. Males also have red leg hair but no pollen baskets
5. Males have two dusky straw bands at the front and back of the thorax

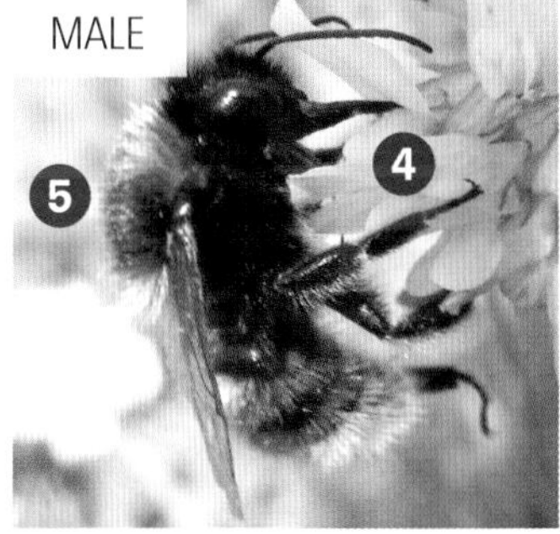

Found in white clover meadows

Tongue length and flowers visited

This bee has a medium length tongue and likes flowers such as Red Clover, White dead-nettle, Ground Ivy, Bird's-foot trefoil and Knapweed.

How to recognise queens and workers

THORAX Black.
ABDOMEN Black.
TAIL Orange-red.
A key feature of this bumblebee is the fringe of orange-red hairs on the hind leg. These hairs give the bee its common name: the Red-Shanked carder bee.

How to recognise males

THORAX Males have a black head but sometimes with some pale hairs. The thorax is black with a dull, dusky straw band at the top and bottom.
ABDOMEN The top part of the abdomen is black with dull, dusky yellow-white hairs to varying extents.
TAIL Orange-red. The red-haired hind legs are the same as in queens and workers.
HEAD Black hairs on face.

What other species look similar?

Red-tailed bumblebee Queens and workers have black hairs on the hind legs around the pollen baskets (red in the Red-shanked carder) and males have yellow facial hair (black in the Red-shanked carder).
Red-tailed cuckoo bee Has very dark wing membranes compared to clear in the Red-shanked carder. Males can be very similar but has a square head, hairier hind legs, and usually has pale grey-yellow bands on the abdomen as well as the thorax.
Early bumblebee Males have yellow facial hair compared to black in the Red-shanked carder.

What other species look similar?	*Bilberry bumblebee* Males have yellow facial hair compared to black in the Red-shanked carder.
Cuckoo	It is thought the Field cuckoo bumblebee may use the Red-shanked carder as its European host.

Female Red-tailed bumblebees (above) have a rich, red tail and black pollen basket hairs on the hind leg

The female Red-shanked carder (above) shows the orange hairs on the pollen baskets

Confusion can occur with Early males (above) but Earlies have much brighter yellow bands

The male Red-shanked carder (above) shows the faint yellow bands on the abdomen

The Early bumblebee *Bombus pratorum*

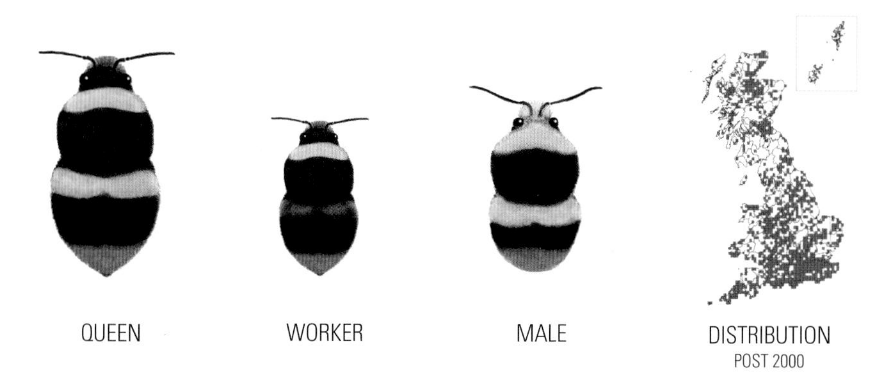

Where to find the Early bumblebee	*This is one of the Big Seven.* Widespread across the UK, except the Outer Hebrides and Northern Isles. *Habitat:* Frequently found in gardens and parks.
When the queens emerge	From March onwards.
Where they nest	Mainly in old rodent nests.
Their lifecycle	In northern UK there is only one generation per year, but in the south they will almost certainly have two. They have fewer than 100 workers within a colony.
Tongue length and flowers visited	The Early Bumblebee has a short tongue. It forages on blackcurrants, Blackberry, raspberries, White Clover, White dead-nettle and Borage.

Q JAN FEB MAR APR MAY JUN JUL AUG SEP OCT NOV DEC

W

M

❶ Both females and males have a yellow band at the top of both the thorax and the abdomen

Queens and workers always have black facial hairs

Remember, this is the UK's smallest bumblebee

❷ In some workers, the band at the top of the abdomen can be missing

❸ Males *always* have a distinctive yellow face

❹ Males have much longer hair

❺ Queens, workers and males *always* have a red tail

Found on early flowers such as *Pulmonaria*, *Primula* and *Muscari*

How to recognise queens, workers and males

THORAX One yellow band at the top. Males often have a small brush of yellow hairs at the back.
ABDOMEN A yellow band at the front. Workers often have this thinned out or completely missing.
TAIL A small red/ginger coloured tail.
NB Males have longer hair and a yellow face.

What other species look similar?

Red-tailed bumblebee Males have no yellow abdominal bands and females have no yellow bands at all.
Bilberry bumblebee The red tail covers more than half of the abdomen (usually just the last abdominal section in the Early bumblebee). There is no yellow abdominal band, which is usually present in Earlies.

Cuckoo

The Forest cuckoo bee will use the Early bumblebee as a host.

An Early male (above) shows the distinctive yellow facial hair

A male (above) showing yellow bands and red tail

Male Red-tailed bumblebees (left) can look similar to Early males. They share a yellow face, but in the Red-tail the second yellow band is on the thorax not the abdomen

The male Bilberry bumblebee (left) could be confused with an Early male but again both bands are on the thorax and the red extends much further up the abdomen

Favourite forage for Earlies includes garden flowers like Flowering Currant, Wallflowers (particularly Bowle's Mauve), geraniums and Lungwort

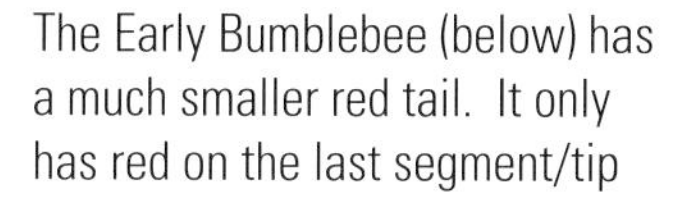

The Early Bumblebee (below) has a much smaller red tail. It only has red on the last segment/tip

Male Broken-belted bumblebees (left) can be mistaken for Early males because they have a peachy-white tail. Their facial hair is always black, while in the Earlies it is yellow

Typical Early forage includes *Pulmonaria* and snowdrops

The Bilberry bumblebee *Bombus monticola*

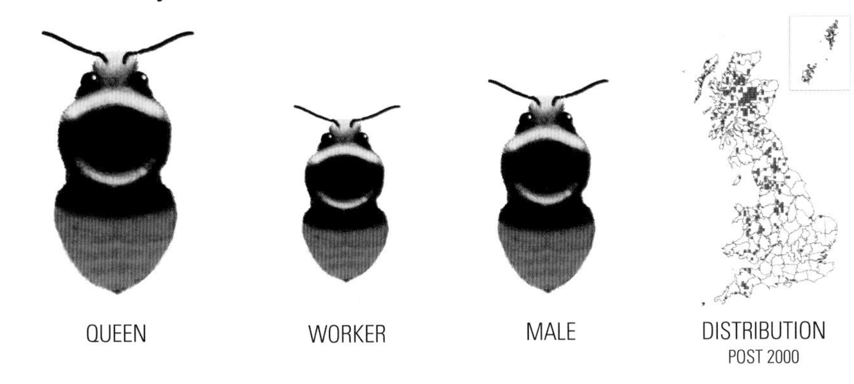

Where to find the Bilberry Bumblebee

This is a less common species. This bumblebee is mainly found in the north and west of the country, across much of upland Wales, the north and west of England and Scotland. It tends to be found at altitudes greater than 300m but can forage at sea level. There has been a decline in the distribution of this species across its range. *Habitat:* Upland areas like moorlands and mountains, but also grasslands.

When the queens emerge

Queens emerge in April and workers can be seen from May. Males and new queens can be seen from mid-July onwards.

Where they nest

Nests are built on the ground surface, or just below, in tall, tussocky grassland.

Their lifecycle

Small colonies of about 50 - 70 workers, seen mostly from mid-June onwards. New queens and males appear in late August to September.

Q JAN FEB MAR APR MAY JUN JUL AUG SEP OCT NOV DEC
W
M

1. Look for the large red tail
2. Two yellow bands at front and back of the thorax
3. The second yellow band is thinner
4. Red hairs will cover half, or more, of the abdomen
5. Males and workers have the same markings as the queens
6. Favourite forage: Bilberry and heathland plants
7. Remember, males have longer hair than females

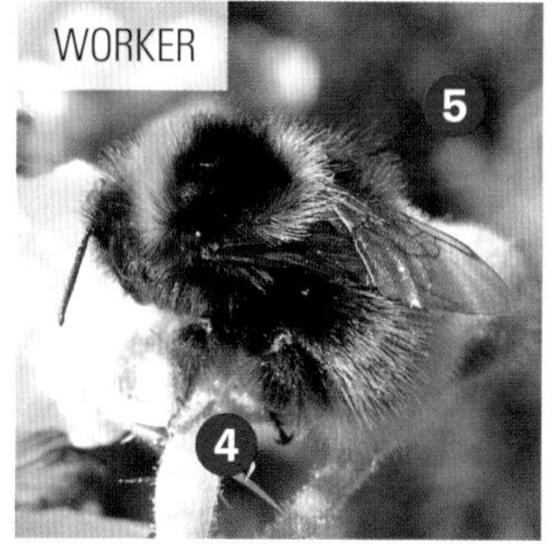

Found on uplands, moors and mountains

Tongue length and flowers visited A long-tongued bumblebee. Its favourite plants include Bilberry, bird's-foot trefoils, heathers and raspberries.

How to recognise queens workers and males THORAX Black with a yellow band at the top and bottom.

ABDOMEN Black.

TAIL A large red tail extending over half the abdomen.

FACE Yellow.

NB Males have longer hair and a brighter yellow face.

What other species look similar? *Early bumblebee* The red tail only covers the last section (more than half for the Bilberry).

Red-tailed bumblebee Females have no yellow bands. Males have yellow thoracic bands, but the red of the tail covers less than half the abdomen. In the Bilberry bumblebee the red tail covers more than half the abdomen.

Host The Forest cuckoo bee uses the Bilberry bumblebee as a host.

A male Early (left) and a Red-tailed male (right) can look similar to Bilberry males. However the red on their tails only covers the final section of the abdomen

This Bilberry male (left) shows the thicker band at the back of the thorax and absence of yellow on the abdomen. The red on its tail extends right up over the abdomen

A queen Bilberry bumblebee clearly showing the bright red colouring of the tail extending up, over almost half the abdomen

The Forest cuckoo bee (left) parasitises the Bilberry bumblebee and so looks similar, but its tail is white with a much smaller red tip

Favourite forage includes bilberries (shown below) heathers, raspberries and clovers

The Common carder bee *Bombus pascuorum*

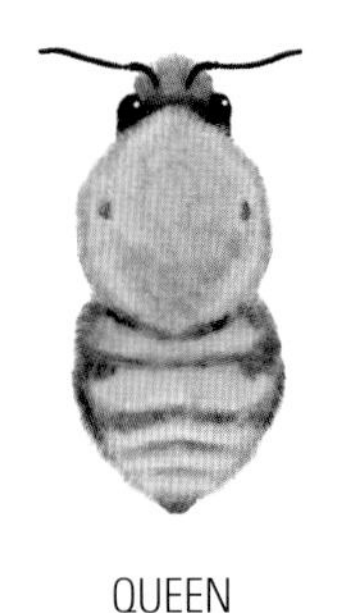

QUEEN

WORKER

MALE

DISTRIBUTION
POST 2000

Where to find the Common carder bee

This is one of the Big Seven. A widespread common species, found almost everywhere in the UK. *Habitat*: Parks, gardens, farms, woodland edges and meadows.

When the queens emerge

March onwards.

Where they nest

On the ground surface, often in tall open grassland, under hedges or at the edge of woodlands. They use pieces of moss and grass for nesting material.

Their lifecycle

Colonies can live for up to 6 months and have 100-150 workers. Workers can be seen flying in October or November when the weather is mild. New queens and males emerge from September onwards.

Q JAN FEB MAR APR MAY JUN JUL AUG SEP OCT NOV DEC
W
M

1. Remember the thorax and abdomen have bright ginger/ yellow-brown hair
2. Common carder bees have long 'shaggy' hair
3. The thorax and abdomen have varying amounts of black hair
4. Workers are much smaller than queens and males
5. Note pollen baskets on the leg
6. Male carders have the same markings as queens and workers
7. This species can be very variable in the colour patterns

Found in gardens and flower-rich meadows

Tongue length and flowers visited

They have a long tongue and their favourite flowers are foxgloves, figworts, clovers, vetches and thistles.

How to recognise queens workers and males

THORAX Covered by yellow-brown or gingery hair. This tends to be scruffy. Black hairs are also mixed in with the ginger.
ABDOMEN Covered by yellow-brown or gingery hair. This tends to be thin, long and scruffy. Black hairs are mixed in but the amount varies, from forming a band, to just being scattered on the sides.
TAIL Ginger.

In Scotland this bumblebee can be much paler and may only have a few black hairs present on the body, you will need a hand lens to have a closer look.

What other species look similar?

Brown-banded carder bee No black hairs on the abdomen and has a ginger-brown band on the second abdominal section.
Moss carder bee No black hairs at all and has a neat and short coat of hair on the thorax.
Shrill carder bee Has an even black band between the wing bases, on top of the thorax, and has straw-yellow bands on the thorax and abdomen.
Tree bumblebee has a white tail compared to the ginger abdomen and tail of the Common carder.

Cuckoo

The Field cuckoo bee uses this bee as a host.

Confusion can happen between Common carder bees and the Brown-banded carder (left). Brown-banded carders have no black hairs on the abdomen and have a distinct brown abdominal band

The Moss carder bee (left) is another cause of confusion. There are however no black hairs on the abdomen The Moss carder bee's coat is neat and short all over with a velvety pile

The male Common carder bee (left) is very faded and you may need a magnifying hand lens to spot the black hairs. The coat is a lot shaggier and longer than on the other Carder bees

A Common carder bee (left) can be confirmed by the scattered black hairs on the abdomen. This is backed up by the longer face. The pollen baskets confirm she is a female. Her size indicates whether she's a queen

The Common carder (above) clearly shows black hairs on the abdomen

The Common carder bee prefers to forage on tubular or trumpet-shaped flowers. It favours foxgloves, thistles, Viper's Bugloss and Clover. It has a long tongue and so can access the nectar at the bottom of the flower without any difficulty

The Moss carder bee *Bombus muscorum*

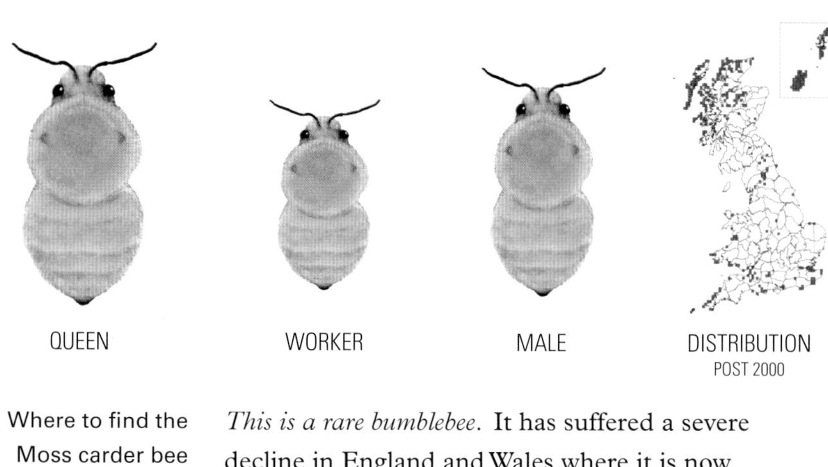

Where to find the Moss carder bee	*This is a rare bumblebee.* It has suffered a severe decline in England and Wales where it is now fairly coastal. It is more common in the north and Scotland, where it can be found across the highlands and islands. *Habitat:* Flowery grasslands, marshes and moors.
When the queens emerge	April-May.
Where they nest	On the ground surface or just below and in open grassland.
Their lifecycle	The colony lives for about three months and usually has no more than 100 workers.
Tongue length and flowers visited	This is a long-tongued bee. It likes Red Clover, bird's-foot trefoils, White dead-nettle, knapweeds, vetches and thistles.

Q W M JAN FEB MAR APR MAY JUN JUL AUG SEP OCT NOV DEC

1. Look for short, neat ginger/ blonde hair. The thorax may have a ring of pale blond hair around the edge

2. There are no black hairs on the body at all

3. Don't mistake dark chitin showing between hairs for black hair

4. Workers have the same colour markings but are smaller than males and queens

5. Males don't have pollen baskets on their hind legs

6. Males are larger than workers

Found in flower-rich meadows

How to recognise queens, workers and males

THORAX Short gingery-brown hair which looks neat, even and velvety and *never* has any black hairs.
ABDOMEN This is covered with yellow-brown hair and lacks *any* black hair. The abdomen is an even blonde/ginger and occasionally has a brown band near the top of the abdomen.
TAIL Ginger.

Island forms: Moss carder bees on the Hebrides, Shetland, Scilly, Aran and Channel Islands have the legs, undersides of the thorax and abdomen, head and thorax sides entirely black-haired, with the top of the thorax and sides & top of the abdomen dark ginger.

What other species look similar?

Common carder bee Has longer, scruffier hair and some black hair on both the thorax and abdomen (Moss carder has no black hairs on the body).
Brown-banded carder bee Has scattered black hairs around the wing bases, which are absent in the Moss carder, and a ginger-brown band on the second abdominal section. Brown-banded and Moss carder males can be very hard to distinguish when faded.
Shrill carder bee Has an even black band between the wing bases, on top of the thorax and has straw-yellow bands on the thorax and abdomen.

Cuckoo

The Field cuckoo bee uses this bee as a host.

The Common carder bee (left) can be distinguished from the Moss carder bee by its long, shaggy hair and by the abundance of black hair on the abdomen

The Moss carder bee queen (left) shows a ring of pale, blonde hair around the thorax, which, when present, can help with identification

The Moss carder bee (above) shows a very neat and velvet-like coat with no black hair visible on the body at all. It can be very hard to tell the Moss from the Brown-banded carder when they are faded, but the presence or absence of black hair at the wing bases is the key

Confusion is easy between Moss and Brown-banded carders as the Moss carder bees can have a pale brown band at the top of the abdomen shown (left)

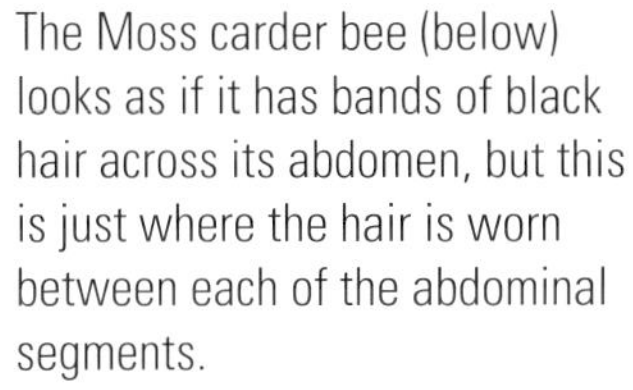

The Moss carder bee (below) looks as if it has bands of black hair across its abdomen, but this is just where the hair is worn between each of the abdominal segments.
Looking closely with a hand lens will help, as will looking across the pile of the hair to see its true colour

The Brown-banded carder (left) can be distinguished by the sparse black hairs at the base of the wings

The Brown-banded carder bee *Bombus humilis*

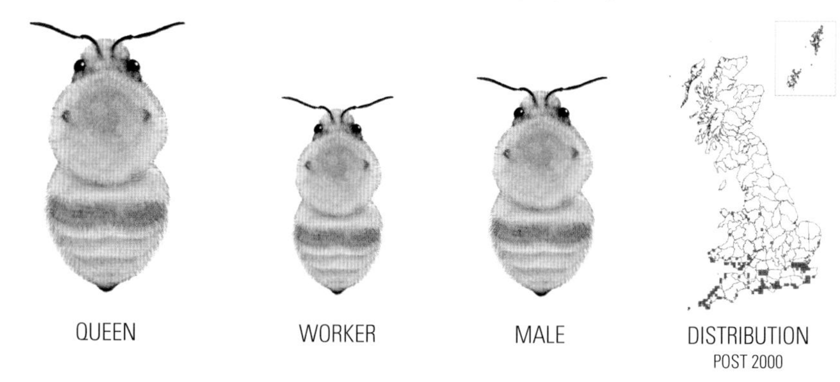

Where to find the Brown-banded carder bee

This is a Rare Bumblebee. This bumblebee has declined significantly in the UK and is now one of the UK's rarest bumblebee species, although there have been recent signs that it may be recovering. It is found mainly in coastal areas along the south of England and Wales and in some inland areas. *Habitat:* It strongly favours flower-rich meadows.

When the queens emerge

May onwards.

Where they nest

The nest is covered with dead grass and moss by the queen and workers.

Their lifecycle

The lifecycle is 3-4 months with just one cycle per year and less than 100 workers. Males and second generation queens will fly from August onwards.

Q JAN FEB MAR APR MAY JUN JUL AUG SEP OCT NOV DEC
W
M

1. Remember the thorax always has ginger hairs
2. Look for pale blonde hair under the wing base
3. The ginger-brown band on the second abdominal matches the thorax
4. Look for two or three black hairs at the wing base. Sometimes there are just a couple of hairs, you will need a hand lens to check
5. All carder bees have yellow faces but males have longer hair and curved antennae. Male carders can be very difficult to tell apart as they fade quickly

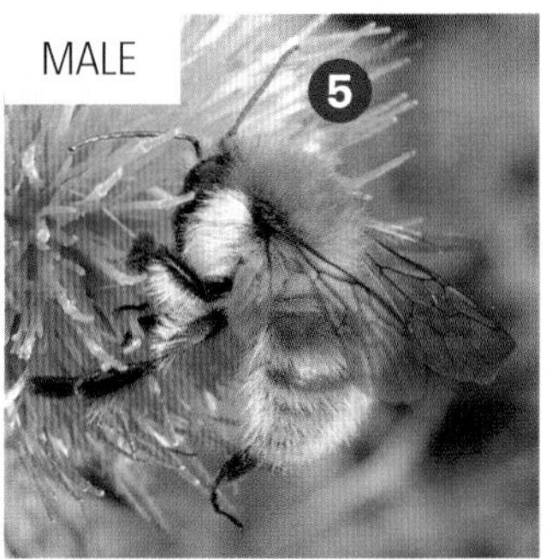

Found in flower-rich meadows

Tongue length and flowers visited

They have a long tongue: found on Red Clover, bird's-foot trefoils, vetches and White dead-nettle.

How to recognise queens, workers and males

THORAX This bumblebee has ginger hair covering the thorax with lighter, ginger/blonde around the sides of the thorax and moving onto the abdomen. There are normally a very few, sometimes only two or three, black hairs just around the base of the wings; you will need a hand lens to have a closer look.
ABDOMEN On the second band of the abdomen there is a strip of ginger hairs, which matches the colour of the ginger thorax.
TAIL The tail is a ginger/blonde.

What other species look similar?

Moss carder bee The Moss carder bee does not have any black hairs on the wing bases or a brown band on the second section of the abdomen (although it sometimes shows a partial ginger band here).
Common carder bee This species has black hairs over the abdomen, in varying amounts, whilst the Brown-banded has none.
Tree bumblebee Could also be confused, but it has a white tail and a brown thorax with a black abdomen.

Cuckoo

This bumblebee is a host to the Forest cuckoo bee.

It is very easy to mistake a Moss carder bee (left) for a Brown-banded carder bee but the Moss carder bee has a short, velvety coat with no black hairs at all

This Common carder bee queen (left) has a pale thorax which might cause confusion, but she has a lot of black hair on her abdomen and no brown band

The brown thorax of the Tree bumblebee (left) could confuse you, if you couldn't see the rest of the body, but the Tree bumblebee abdomen is always black and the tail is always white

The Brown-banded carder (left) will always have a few black hairs at the wing base. Check this with a hand lens

A favourite forage of the Brown-banded carder is White Deadnettle. It flowers early and then may provide a second flush of flowers in the autumn

Distinguishing between the Brown-banded carder and the Moss carder bee is one of the trickiest identification tasks, because they can look very similar. This is especially true with faded specimens

The presence of sparse black hairs at the wing base of the Brown-banded carder will always confirm its species. The Moss carder bee never has any black hair in this area

The Shrill carder bee *Bombus sylvarum*

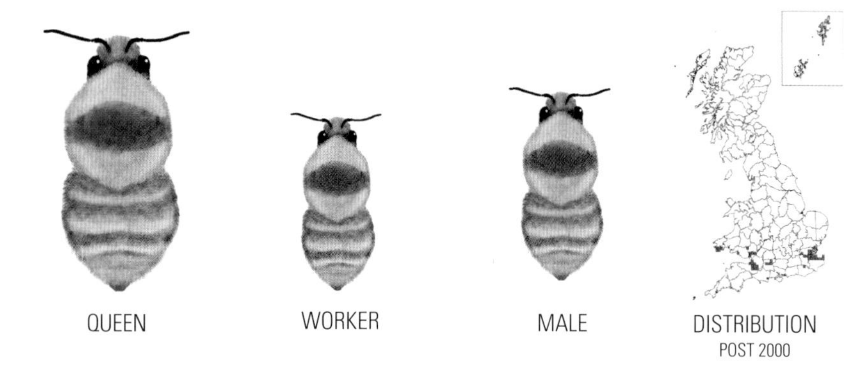

Where to find the Shrill carder bee

This is a very rare bumblebee. Now probably the UK's most endangered bumblebee. The distribution of the Shrill carder bee has seriously decreased in the last 100 years. It is now only found in five scattered populations in Kent, Essex, Somerset, Gwent, Carmarthenshire and Pembrokeshire. *Habitat*: Linked with flower-rich areas on sand dunes, heathlands, edges of salt-marshes, shingle beaches and chalk downs.

When the queens emerge

This is a late-emerging bumblebee, usually seen from May.

Where they nest

Nests are built on the ground surface, or just below, in thick vegetation such as tall or tussocky grassland.

Their lifecycle

Small colonies of about 50 - 70 workers are seen from mid-June onwards. New queens and males appear in late August to September.

Q JAN FEB MAR APR MAY JUN JUL AUG SEP OCT NOV DEC
W
M

1 The Shrill carder has dull, straw/yellow hair

2 Look for the wide black band of hair between the wings

3 The tail is always orange/ginger

4 Workers are much smaller than queens and males. Queens, workers and males all have the same colour markings

5 The tail can sometimes look quite faded

Found in heathlands, saltmarsh, downs and 'brown field' sites

Tongue length and flowers visited

This is a long-tongued bumblebee: favourite plants are White dead-nettle, Hedge Woundwort, Black Horehound, Red Clover and bird's-foot trefoils.

How to recognise queens workers and males

THORAX The thorax is a pale straw-yellow colour with a black band of hair between the wings.
ABDOMEN Pale straw-yellow at the top, with one or two black bands in the middle of the thorax.
TAIL Reddish orange.

This is a relatively small bumblebee. It also has a noticeably high-pitched buzz, sounding more like a honeybee than a bumblebee.

What other species look similar?

Common carder bee Has an all-ginger thorax and abdomen with some scattered black abdominal hair, whereas the Shrill carder has straw-yellow and black bands with an orange tail.
Moss carder bee Has a blonde/ginger thorax, abdomen and tail. It never has the straw-yellow, black bands and orange tail of the Shrill carder.
Brown-banded carder bee Has a completely ginger/blonde thorax compared to the straw-yellow and black banding of the Shrill carder. These bees also have a ginger-brown band on the second abdominal section.
Early bumblebee The yellow bands are much brighter, a lemon-yellow compared to the straw-yellow bands of the Shrill carder.

Cuckoo

This bumblebee is thought to be a host to the Forest cuckoo bee.

The Shrill carder (left) has the classic markings; dull straw bands, a wide black thoracic band and an orange tail. The tail can fade over time and become much paler

The Shrill carder is the UK's most endangered bumblebee. It is mainly found on flower-rich grasslands and brownfield sites (above)
It is so rare, that it is unlikely you will ever come across it in your garden or local park.
If you want to see the Shrill carder you will have to go to an existing 'known site' to have a chance of finding one

Shrill carders can be confused with other Carders such as the Common male (left) but none of the others have the strong black band across the thorax

Confusion is easy with Moss and Brown-banded carders too, but they are ginger and the Shrill carder is a straw-yellow colour (see top)

The Shrill carder bee could be confused with a faded Early bumblebee male (left) because they share a red tail and have a stripe of black hair on the thorax

However, the Shrill carder has two thick pale thoracic bands, while the Early only has one thick band. Remember, the Shrill carder's face is straw-coloured while the Early male will have bright yellow hair on the face and shoulders

The Great Yellow bumblebee *Bombus distinguendus*

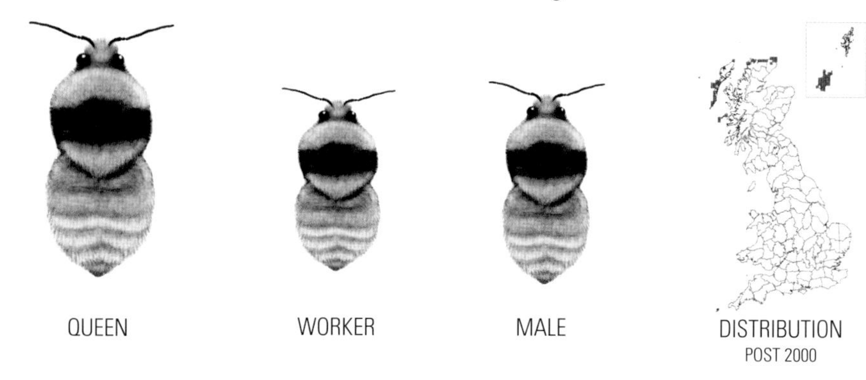

Where to find the Great Yellow bumblebee	*This is a very rare bumblebee.* Until the 1960's it was found all over the UK, although not abundantly. Population and range have declined seriously and now it is only found in Caithness and Sutherland in the far north and west of Scotland, on Orkney and in some of the Hebrides. *Habitat:* Now largely restricted to the machair grasslands. Found in wildflower meadows and occasionally in gardens.
When the queens emerge	Queens emerge quite late, from around mid-May.
Where they nest	In old rodent holes.
Their lifecycle	The colony will go on until September and even October when the weather is fine. The nests have few workers usually between 50-80.

Q JAN FEB MAR APR MAY JUN JUL AUG SEP OCT NOV DEC

W

M

1. Remember the hairs on the middle band of the thorax are always black. Don't mistake worn hairs and visible chitin for black hairs
2. Two yellow bands at top and bottom of thorax
3. Abdomen is all a bright yellow
4. Females and males share the same colour pattern
5. Pollen baskets on the leg show a queen or a worker
6. Males have longer antennae than females, no pollen baskets and a longer abdomen
7. Males and workers similar sizes. Both are smaller than queens

Found on machair and wildflower meadows

Tongue length and flowers visited

These are long-tongued bumblebees. They favour Red Clover, bird's-foot trefoils, vetches and Black Knapweed.

How to recognise queens workers,and males

All castes have the same colour pattern

THORAX There are two yellow bands at the top and bottom of the thorax with a black band between the wings.

ABDOMEN All yellow.

TAIL The yellow is a fairly bright, even colour and looks the same shade on all the bands where it is present.

What other species look similar?

White-tailed bumblebee Males have a white tail compared to the yellow of the Great Yellow.

Common carder bee Ginger/brown in colour rather than golden-yellow.

Field cuckoo bee Males look similar but have a dark central streak down the top of the abdomen. Additionally, the ranges do not overlap.

Short-haired bumblebee Males look similar, but the ranges do not overlap.

Cuckoo

It is possible the Field cuckoo may have once used the nests of the Great Yellow in the past, but their ranges no longer overlap.

Confusion might occur with a White -tailed male (left) but Great Yellow bumblebees never have a white tail

This Moss carder bee queen could be confused with a Great Yellow but the Great Yellow will always have a large black band on the thorax between the wings

The Common carder bee could be confused with the Great Yellow but the former has ginger hair on the thorax and no bold black band

The Great Yellow bumblebee (left) clearly shows the bold black stripe between the wings and the two yellow thoracic bands

It is unlikely that you will confuse the Great Yellow bumblebee with any other bee. It is found on flower-rich grassland in the north and west of Scotland and the Scottish islands, outside the ranges of several 'confusion species'

The Southern cuckoo bee *Bombus vestalis*

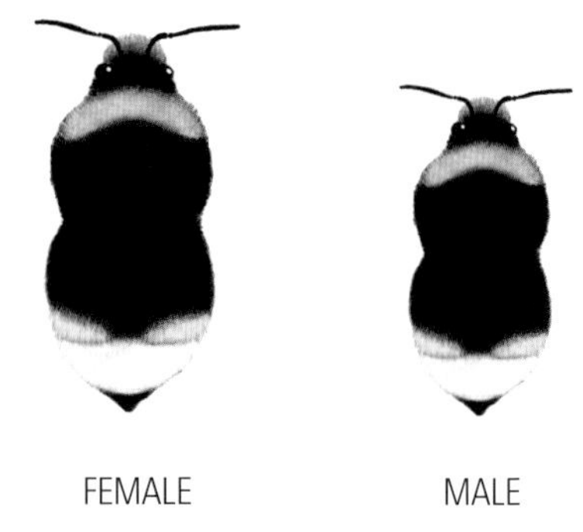

FEMALE MALE

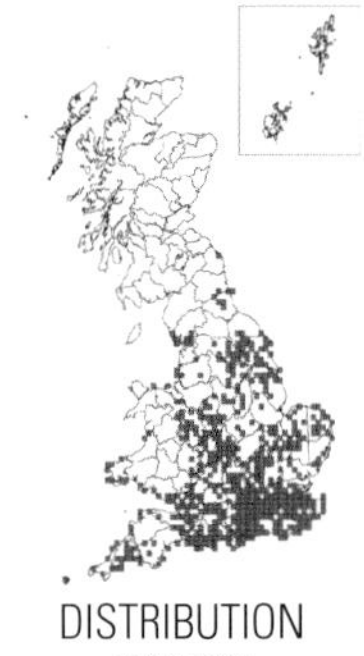

DISTRIBUTION
POST 2000

Where to find the Southern cuckoo bee

This is a cuckoo bumblebee. These bees are quite common throughout most of England, especially in the south. They can be found more scarcely throughout Wales and further north. They have recently been found in Ireland in 2014, having not been recorded there since 1926. *Habitat:* Found in a range of habitat, wild flower meadows and gardens.

When the females emerge

Females emerge in May and new females and males will fly in September.

Where they nest

They will actively seek out a nest of their host species: the Buff-tailed bumblebee.

Their lifecycle

New females and males will usually emerge from May onwards and be flying until September.

Tongue length and flowers visited

These are short-tongued bees. They visit Blackberry, dandelions, Blackthorn, knapweeds, Lavender, wallflowers, White Clover, garden flowers and Cherry.

Q JAN FEB MAR APR MAY JUN JUL AUG SEP OCT NOV DEC
M

1. Look for the single, dark yellow band on the thorax
2. Females don't collect pollen. They have a different structure on the hind leg
3. Look for the pale yellow side patches on the abdomen at the top of the white tail
4. The wings may be darker than in 'true' social bumblebees
5. Cuckoo legs are typically round and hairy
6. Remember the front band is darker than the yellow tail bands

Found in gardens, meadows and hedgerows

How to recognise females	THORAX Dark yellow band at the top of the thorax, then black hairs. ABDOMEN Black abdomen. TAIL White with two yellow patches on either side at the top of the tail.
How to recognise males	THORAX Dark yellow band at the top of the thorax and then black hairs. ABDOMEN Black, often with a faint yellow band across the top of the abdomen. TAIL White with two yellow patches on either side at the top of the tail.
What other species look similar?	*Gypsy cuckoo* Yellow markings on the thorax and above the tail are a lighter sandy colour compared to lemon-yellow in the Southern cuckoo. Male Gypsy cuckoos also have longer hair.
Host	The Buff-tailed bumblebee.

The Southern cuckoo bee is trying to look like its host the Buff-tailed bumblebee (left). However the Buff-tail has a yellow band on the abdomen

The Southern cuckoo tail is pure white with pale yellow bands only at the top. The Buff-tail's tail (left) is buff/orange and is separated from the yellow band by a black stripe

The White-tailed bumblebee (above) has a pure-white tail just like the Southern cuckoo, but without yellow side patches. Like the Buff-tail, its white tail and yellow band are separated by a black stripe. The Southern cuckoo will always have yellow hairs above its white tail

With wings closed the Southern cuckoo (left) may be confused with a Buff-tail, but the wings are much too dark for a 'true' social bee

A Southern cuckoo has a dark yellow thoracic band, white tail and pale yellow bands sitting on top of the white tail

The Gypsy cuckoo (above) looks similar to the Southern cuckoo, but has a second yellow band on the thorax and a shaggier appearance. Gypsy cuckoos are more common in the north

The Field cuckoo bee *Bombus campestris*

Where to find the Field cuckoo bee	*This a cuckoo bumblebee.* Widespread across England and Wales but can be localised. In Scotland it is limited to the south with occasional records in the Highlands. *Habitat*: Found in gardens, hedgerows and flower rich meadows.
When the females emerge	April onwards.
Where they nest	Because this species is a cuckoo no workers are produced. It will find a surface nest of a carder bee to parasitise.
Their lifecycle	New queens and males will fly from July to September. This bumblebee will have one cycle per year.
Tongue length and flowers visited	This is a short-tongued species favouring White Clover, thistles, Blackberry, knapweeds and Teasel.

Q JAN FEB MAR APR MAY JUN JUL AUG SEP OCT NOV DEC
M

1. Two yellow bands on the thorax
2. Black hair all over the abdomen, with chitin visible between the wing bases
3. This is the only cuckoo bee with a yellow tail
4. Males have a third band of yellow hair at the very top of the abdomen
5. Males' yellow tails extend half way up the abdomen
6. Dark form males are all black, but may show a few yellow tail hairs

Found in flower-rich meadows

How to recognise females

THORAX Two yellow bands on the thorax at the top and bottom with some back hairs between the wing bases. The chitin can be seen in the black band.
ABDOMEN Black.
TAIL Yellow.

How to recognise males

LIGHT FORM
THORAX Two yellow bands on the thorax at the top and bottom with some back hairs between the wing bases. The chitin can be seen in the black band.
ABDOMEN: The top abdominal band has tufted yellow hairs.
TAIL Yellow.
DARK FORM
THORAX All black.
ABDOMEN All black.
TAIL Black but will sometimes have yellow hairs present.

What other species look similar?

Great Yellow bumblebee Males look similar but do not have a central black streak on the top of the abdomen and their ranges do not overlap.
Ruderal bumblebee Dark-form male Ruderals have a much longer face and females have pollen baskets (not present in the cuckoo).

Host

This species is likely to use all carder bees.

A dark form Ruderal male (left) could be easily mistaken for a dark form of the Field cuckoo male. You need a hand lens to look closely at the structure of the leg. In the 'true' social bumblebee the legs are covered in short, stubbly hairs. On the cuckoo the hair is much longer and there is a 'barb' on the hind leg. Cuckoos also commonly have chitin showing through the hair on their abdomen. This will appear shiny and black

The Great Yellow male (left) has yellow hairs all over the abdomen but the Field cuckoo male has black hairs at the top of the abdomen

The Field cuckoo is the only cuckoo bee where the female (left) has a yellow tail. The tail is small and at the tip of the abdomen

The Forest cuckoo male (left) might be confused with a Field cuckoo male but the Forest cuckoo has red hairs at the tip of the tail

The Field cuckoo can be found in gardens and hedgerows (above)

The Gypsy cuckoo bee *Bombus bohemicus*

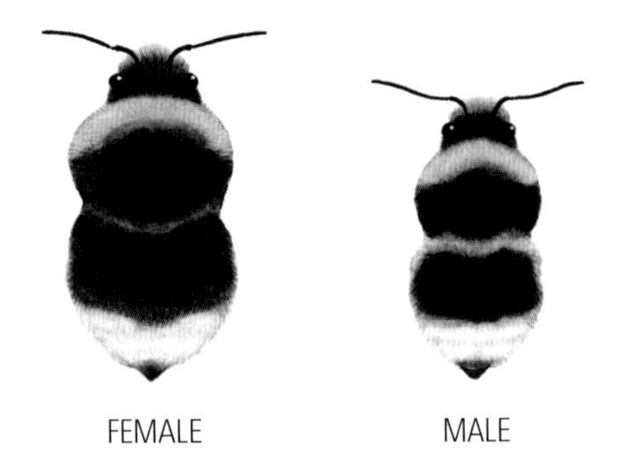

FEMALE MALE

DISTRIBUTION
POST 2000

Where to find the Gypsy cuckoo bee

This is a cuckoo bumblebee. This bee is mainly found in the north and west, although it appears to be undergoing a long-term decline in the south and east. *Habitat*: Heath, moorland and upland areas.

When the females emerge

April to May.

Where they nest

These cuckoo bees seek out a nest of their hosts, the White-tailed bumblebee complex, usually in a disused rodent burrow.

Their lifecycle

Males and new females will emerge from June. They have usually disappeared by the end of August. Some males may be visible into September.

Tongue length and flowers visited

This is a short-tongued species which visits thistles, brambles, umbellifers, knapweeds and teasels.

Q JAN FEB MAR APR MAY JUN JUL AUG SEP OCT NOV DEC
M

1. The female has a thick yellow top band on the thorax and a faint yellow bottom band
2. Female cuckoos are larger than the male
3. The Gypsy cuckoo has longer hair than other cuckoos
4. Bald patches of chitin are visible on the thorax and the abdomen
5. Both females and males have a white tail with small yellow bands at the sides of the abdomen at the top of the tail

Found on heathland

How to recognise females

THORAX A thick, obvious yellow band at the top of the thorax, with a small brush of yellow hairs at the bottom. A strong black band between the wing bases, with some chitin visible.
ABDOMEN Black.
TAIL White, with two yellow side patches.

How to recognise males

THORAX Two yellow bands at the top and bottom of the thorax with black hairs between the wing bases.
ABDOMEN The top of the abdomen has tufted yellow and black hairs, then a black band before the tail.
TAIL White, with two yellow side-patches at the top.

What other bees look similar

Southern cuckoo bee Has bright lemon-yellow bands compared to the paler banding of the Gypsy cuckoo. It also has shorter, neater hair than the Gypsy cuckoo.

Host

The species uses the White-tailed bumblebee complex.

The female Gypsy cuckoo bee (left) has a characteristic 'boxy' head This shape holds true for all cuckoo bees

Gypsy cuckoo bees are most likely to be found on heathland and upland sites. Their favoured forage includes thistles, brambles and knapweeds

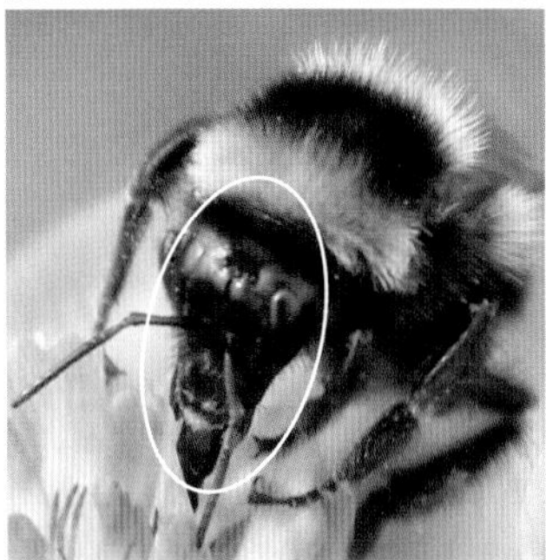

This Garden bumblebee might cause confusion with the Gypsy cuckoo, because it has similar markings. However the Garden has a very long face

The Garden bumblebee (left) has dense hair. Cuckoos typically have sparser hair, so the shiny, black chitin shows through from underneath

The Gypsy cuckoo bee (left) shows characteristic 'bald' patches on the thorax and abdomen, where the exoskeleton is showing through the thin hair

The Red-tailed cuckoo bee *Bombus rupestris*

FEMALE

MALE

DISTRIBUTION
POST 2000

Where to find the Red-tailed cuckoo bee	*This a cuckoo bumblebee.* Widespread in southern England, becoming sparser further north and west. Appears to be spreading northwards, with a first Scottish record in 2013. *Habitat:* Open grasslands, woodlands and gardens.
When the bees emerge	April to June.
Where they nest	They take over the nests of the Red-tailed bumblebee, usually underground or in enclosed locations.
Their lifecycle	Females emerge from hibernation April-June and take over Red-tailed bumblebee nests. The males and new queens are on the wing in July and August.

Q JAN FEB MAR APR MAY JUN JUL AUG SEP OCT NOV DEC
M

1. Note the red tail extends well up the abdomen

2. Cuckoo bees often have very dark wings in comparison to the clear wings of 'true' social bumblebees

3. The hair is sparse and a lot of chitin shines through from the exoskeleton

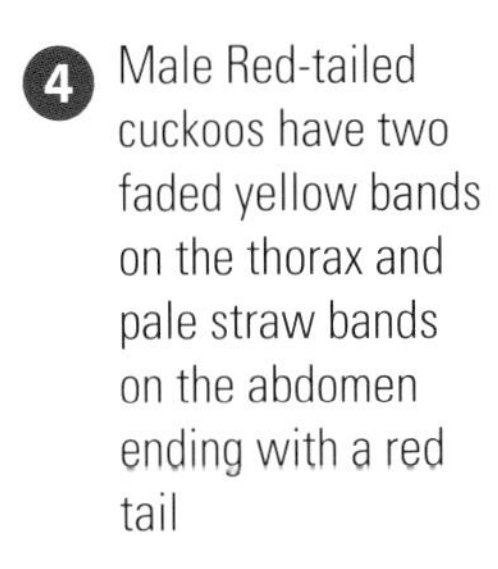

4. Male Red-tailed cuckoos have two faded yellow bands on the thorax and pale straw bands on the abdomen ending with a red tail

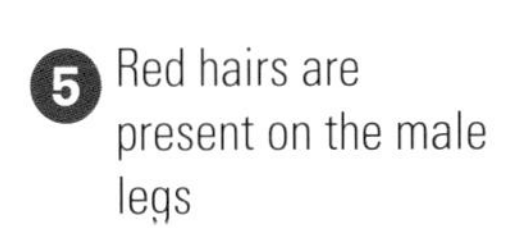

5. Red hairs are present on the male legs

Found in gardens

Tongue length and flowers visited	This is a short-tongued bumblebee. It visits composite flowers like dandelions, Oxeye daisy, thistles and brambles.
How to recognise females	THORAX All black. ABDOMEN Black. TAIL Red.
How to recognise males	THORAX Black with faint, washed-out, straw-coloured bands at the top and bottom. ABDOMEN Black with pale bands. TAIL Orange/red.
What other species look similar?	*Red-tailed bumblebee* Females have clear wing membranes (dark in the Red-tailed cuckoo) as well as pollen baskets. Males of the Red-tailed have yellow facial hair. *Red-shanked carder bee* Females have clear wing membranes (dark in the Red-tailed cuckoo), as well as pollen baskets. Red-tailed cuckoos also have a much squarer head. *Bilberry bumblebee* Females have clear wing membranes (dark in the Red-tailed cuckoo), as well as pollen baskets. Males have yellow facial hair compared to black in Red-tailed cuckoos.
Host	The Red-tailed bumblebee.

The Red-tailed cuckoo bee is often confused with a Red-tailed bumblebee (left). The differences are subtle, but can be spotted. The wings of the Red-tailed bumblebee are clear, but those of the cuckoo are very dark. The red on the tail is clear and bright in a Red-tailed bumblebee, whereas the cuckoo's tail is a much more orangey red. Finally the hind leg of the 'true' social bumblebee clearly shows a flat, shiny pollen basket with lots of long hairs

The Red-tailed cuckoo (left) shows the very dark wings that indicate this species. The body shape is long with a deep, boxy face. The cuckoo's tail colour extends much further up the abdomen, which often looks quite ridged. Finally the hind legs are round and covered with short hairs. There are no pollen baskets because cuckoos don't collect pollen

The Red-tailed cuckoo male (left), looks very similar to the Red-shanked carder male (right). However the carder bee has brighter red leg hair and the cuckoo's hind legs are hairier

Don't worry if you see small, bead-shaped pale mites on bumblebees; these do not harm the bee. Nest-cleaning mites live in the bottom of bumblebee nests and live by clearing up detritus from the bee's nest. They hitch a ride on the bee's back and then drop down to the bottom of the nest and start cleaning up. While mites may not look very appealing, they are helping and not harming the bee

The Forest cuckoo bee *Bombus sylvestris*

FEMALE

MALE

DISTRIBUTION
POST 2000

Where to find the Forest cuckoo bee	*This a cuckoo bumblebee.* This species is widely distributed across Britain and can be very common in some areas. *Habitat:* Parks and gardens, heathland and moorland.
When the females emerge	April to June.
Where they nest	Usually parasitises the nests of the Early bumblebee, but also attacks Heath and Bilberry bumblebees.
Their lifecycle	This is the earliest-emerging cuckoo species as it primarily attacks the early-nesting Early bumblebee. Males and new queens emerge from May and can be locally-abundant throughout June. Hosts have two generations per year and this species may also be able to achieve this. Very few records after August.
Tongue length and flowers visited	This species has a short tongue and feeds on a variety of flower species including dead-nettles, dandelions, thistles, brambles and Scabious.

Q JAN FEB MAR APR MAY JUN JUL AUG SEP OCT NOV DEC
M

1. Note the broad yellow band at the front of the thorax. There is a second faint gold band at the top of the abdomen

2. Females have a narrow band of yellow hairs above the white tail

3. These are the UK's smallest cuckoos. They are often the first to appear, as the life cycle of their host, the Early bumblebee, begins early and is short

4. The most distinctive feature is the tail. It is white, with a black band and an orange tip

5. The orange tip is very small and easy to miss

Found on brambles, thistles and White dead-nettle

How to recognise females

THORAX Black with a strong yellow band on the top of the thorax.

ABDOMEN Black with faint yellow band at the top.

TAIL White.

How to recognise males

THORAX Black with a strong yellow band on the top of the thorax.

ABDOMEN Black with faint yellow band at the top.

TAIL White followed by visible red hairs on the end of the tail.

NB: Some males have a yellow or buff-coloured tail, but still have the red tail tip.

What other species look similar?

Barbut's cuckoo bee but this species can be distinguished by an obvious yellow band at the bottom of the thorax. It is a larger bumblebee.

Field cuckoo bee is similar, but this species has a yellow/buff tail with a black tip; it is never red/orange like Forest cuckoo males.

Host

The Early bumblebee, the Heath bumblebee and the Bilberry bumblebee.

The male Field cuckoo bee (left) could be confused with a Forest cuckoo bee but their tails are different. The Field has a yellow tail, while the Forest has a white tail with an orange tip

Barbut's cuckoo has an obvious second yellow band at the bottom of the thorax. This distinguishes it from the Forest cuckoo which only has a top band. This is a larger bee than the Forest cuckoo

This Forest cuckoo male has red hairs at the base of the tail, but they are difficult to see and you have to look carefully to confirm them

The Field cuckoo bee can be found in a wide range of habitats including woodland edges, open grassland, upland moors and heathland. It forages on a wide variety of flowers including the usual hedgerow inhabitants such as brambles, thistles and dead-nettles. It also visits Scabious flowers

Barbut's cuckoo bee *Bombus barbutellus*

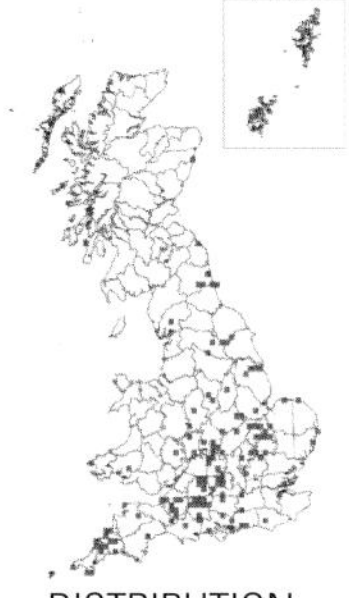

DISTRIBUTION
POST 2000

Where to find Barbut's cuckoo bee

This a cuckoo bumblebee. This species is widespread in south and central England. It is scarcer in the north and is rare in Wales and Scotland. *Habitat:* Found in a wide variety of habitats, though apparently not so widespread as its host.

When the females emerge

April to May.

Where they nest

Usually in the nests of Garden or Ruderal bumblebees.

Their lifecycle

Parasitises the nests of Garden bumblebees and is also likely to use Ruderal bumblebees.

Tongue length and flowers visited

A short-tongued species which visits a wide range of garden and wild flowers for nectar, but not pollen.

Q M JAN FEB MAR APR MAY JUN JUL AUG SEP OCT NOV DEC

1. Remember, like their host species, these are large bees

2. Both females and males have yellow bands at the top and bottom of the thorax and a wide black band between the wing bases

3. Look for faint yellow bands on the abdomen but no yellow side-patches at the front of the white tail

4. Bald patches of hair will reveal the black chitin of the exoskeleton on the abdomen

5. Males have longer hair than females

How to recognise females and males

THORAX Black, with thick yellow bands front and rear.
ABDOMEN Black, with a variable yellow band at the very front.
TAIL White.

What other species look similar?

The Heath, Garden and Ruderal bumblebees are all similar to Barbut's cuckoo bee, having three yellow bands and a white tail. The cuckoo always has a deeper, boxier head and hairier hind legs than the 'true' social species. The cuckoo also has a short, round face (this is long in the Garden and Ruderal bumblebees). The male Heath bumblebee has yellow facial hair, while queens and workers have pollen baskets. Some variations of the Gypsy and Southern cuckoo bees can look similar, but the tail of Barbut's cuckoo is grey-white, with no hint of the yellow side-patches present in those species.

Host

The Garden bumblebee and the Ruderal bumblebee, although its range does not extend as far north as that of the host.

The worker Heath bumblebee (left) looks very similar to a Barbut's cuckoo but 'true' social bumblebee females always have pollen baskets

This Barbut's cuckoo shows the tail as quite a dull white. There are no yellow hairs at the top of the white tail which would be seen in, for example, a Southern cuckoo

The Southern cuckoo bee (left) can be distinguished from the Barbut's cuckoo by a band of yellow hairs that is clear to see above the white tail

This Garden bumblebee could be mistaken for a Barbut's cuckoo but the Garden has long, shaggy hair, while the cuckoo bee's is short and neat

This cuckoo bee is found in meadows and gardens

Finding out more

BUMBLEBEE CONSERVATION TRUST
Everything you need to know about bumblebees and how to set up a BeeWalk
bumblebeeconservation.org
www.beewalk.org.uk

BEES, WASPS AND ANTS RECORDING SOCIETY
Ecology pages on most species
www.bwars.com

NATURAL HISTORY MUSEUM
Identification of all the worlds' bumblebee species
www.nhm.ac.uk/research-curation/research/projects/bombus/index

Further reading

IDENTIFICATION BOOKS

Falk, S. and Lewington, R. (2015) *Field Guide to the Bees of Great Britain and Ireland.* British Wildlife Publishing Ltd.

Prŷs-Jones, O. and Corbet, S. (2011) *Bumblebees* (Naturalists' Handbooks). Pelagic Publishing.

ECOLOGY AND LIFECYCLE BOOKS

Alford, D.V. (1975) *Bumblebees.* Davis-Poynter

Comont, R. F. (2017) *RSPB Spotlight Bumblebees.* Bloomsbury Natural History.

Goulson, D. (2010). *Bumblebees; their behaviour, ecology and conservation.* Oxford University Press, Oxford

Sladen F.W.L. (1912) *The humble bee: its life history and how to domesticate it.* Macmillan and Co., London

GARDENING AND PLANTS FOR BUMBLEBEES

Kirk, W.D.J. and Howes, F.N. (2012) *Plants for bees.* IBRA

EQUIPMENT FOR RECORDING BUMBLEBEES

Watkins and Doncaster www.watdon.com

EH Thorne (Beehives) Ltd www.thorne.co.uk

Glossary

Abdomen (or gaster)
The third and last section of the body, containing the digestive and reproductive organs.

Banding
The coloured stripes that apear on the thorax and abdomen of many bumblebees.

Basitarsus
The mid-section of the bumblebee's lower leg. It is found between the tibia and the tarsus.

BeeWalk
A set route, or transect, which is visited regularly to count and identify bumblebees.

Brush hairs
These are a series of long, stiff hairs found on the tibia of queen and worker bumblebees. The brush hairs are used to help compact pollen into a ball, which then sits on the flat shiny part part of the tibia called the pollen basket.

Bumblebee (true social)
Social bees that live in small nests with one queen and between 50-400 workers. Eighteen of the UK's twenty four species are 'true' social bumblebees.

Buzz pollination
See sonication.

*Carder bee*s
These nest on the ground surface and use grass and moss to create their nests.

Chitin
A thick, horn-like substance that makes up the exoskeleton of bumblebees. Cuckoo bees have an extra thick layer, which acts like armour.

Cold-blooded animal
These creatures cannot control their body temperature.

Compound Eye
The bumblebee's eye is made up of many tiny optical units, each with its own lens. These many units make up each of the two large compound eyes.

Cuckoo bees
Parasite of a social colony, uses workers of the host to feed their offspring. There are six UK species.

Drone
Male Honey bee.

Egg
The first stage of bumblebee development. The egg then hatches into a larva.

Exoskeleton
The hard, outer shell of insects which is made of chitin.
Genus
This is a biological classification within taxonomic ranking. The term Genus is a way of showing that species are closely related to each other. Genus ranks above species and below family.
Fertiliser
Typically a mix of chemicals and minerals used to increase soil nutrients artificially.
Hand lens (or loupe)
A small magnifying glass, sometimes with LED lights, that is easy to carry and enables you to see details more easily.
Head
The bee's head contains the sensory organs; the eyes, the ocelli and the antennae. It also houses the mouthparts and mandibles.
Hibernation
This happens when the bee's body 'shuts down' to save energy over the winter months.
Honey bee
These social bees live in a hive with one queen and between 50-100,000 workers forming a complex perennial society. There is only one species in the UK.
Larva
The second stage in development after the egg. The larva has mouth parts so it can eat pollen.
Mandible
Jaws used to cut, bite, grab food and also used in defence.
Melanistic
The melanistic form of bumblebee is one in which the bee is totally (or almost totally) black in colour.
Nectar
Sugar-rich substance produced by plants to reward visiting insects.
Neonicotinoids
A range of pesticides containing nicotine.
Ocelli
A simple (non-compound) light-sensitive eye, found on the head of a bumblebee.
Ovipositor
Female-only egg-laying organ, also modified into a sting.
Ovule
The part of a plant which houses the germ cells of seeding plants. When fertilised during pollination, they grow into seeds.

Parasitise
When one organism lives in or on another to the detriment of the host. Cuckoo bumblebees parasitise the nests of 'true' bumblebee.
Pesticide
This is a treatment used to kill pest species.
Pollen basket
Female social bees have pollen baskets on their hind legs (tibia) to hold the pollen they collect.
Pollen
Male sex cells produced by a plant. Bees collect pollen to feed to their larvae because it is a rich source of protein.
Pupa
The bee's final development stage before it turns into an adult.
Queen
A female with fully developed ovaries. She can lay male and female eggs. One queen is present in a social colony of bumblebees.
Queen plunger
A device made up of a transparent tube with mesh at one end and a foam-tipped plunger. These were originally developed by bee keepers to mark queen Honey bees. They are often employed in bumblebee identification as they enable you to hold the bee still without harming it.
Solitary bees
These only have males and females. There is no 'worker caste'. There are approximately 240 species of solitary bees in the UK.
Specimen Pot
Small glass or plastic pots, which are transparent and enable you to look closely at a bumblebee.
Spiracle
Tiny holes in the exoskeleton which are used for gas exchange and for cooling the body.
Sonication
Sonication is the term used to describe 'buzz-pollination'. The bumblebee grips the flower with its mandibles and then vibrates its flight muscles to dislodge pollen from plants such as tomatoes.
Stamen
The male part of the flower which produces pollen.
Stigma
The female part of a flower that receives the pollen during pollination.
Swarm
A swarm happens when an old Honey bee queen is usurped. She

leaves the old nest with between 2-5,000 workers to found a new colony. Swarms are often seen in trees and on fence posts.

Tail

The bottom tip of the bee's abdomen, the tail is often a different colour. Look at the tail first when trying to identify a bumblebee.

Tarsus

The tarsus is made up of the final section of the bee's lower leg. It ends in hook-like claws for grasping flowers.

Thorax

The middle part of a bumblebee's body, where wings and legs are attached.

Tibia

Top part of an insect's lower leg.

True bumblebee

This bumblebee forms a social colony with a queen and worker caste.

Wildflower strip

A section of a field that a farmer has planted with a wildflower mix of seeds to encourage wildlife. These areas are not treated with pesticides or fertilisers.

Worker

Workers are females, which, unlike a queen, do not have developed ovaries. They can lay male eggs.

Index

Agri-environment scheme, 41
Abdomen, **18**, 20, 21, 29, 66, **69**
Abdominal band, **19**, **69**
Antenna, 11, **18**, 20, 21
Anther, 32, 34, **35**, 38
Apple bumblebee, 24, 25
Apis melifera see Honey bee
Barbut's cuckoo bee, 63, **64**, 160-163 see *Bombus barbutellus*
Basitarsus, 70, **70,** 71
Bees, Wasps and Ants Recording Society (BWARS), 58, 164
Beeswax, 13, **36**
BeeWalk 58-59
'Big Seven', **62**, 63
Bilberry bumblebee, 63, **64**, 116-119 see *Bombus monticola*
Bombus barbutellus, 63, **64**, 160-163 see Barbut's cuckoo bee
Bombus bohemicus, 63, **64**, 148-151 see Gypsy cuckoo bee
Bombus campestris, 63, **64**, 143, 144-147, see Field cuckoo bee
Bombus distinguendus, 63, **65**, 136-139 see Great Yellow bumblebee
Bombus hortorum, 10, 24, **62**, 63, 68, 69 and 71, 76-79, see Garden bumblebee
Bombus humilis, 41, 63, **65**, 128-131 see Brown-banded carder bee
Bombus hypnorum, **62**, 63, 88-91, see Tree bumblebee
Bombus jonellus, 63, **64**, 78, 80-83, see Heath bumblebee
Bombus lapidarius, **62**, 63, 104-107 see Red-tailed bumblebee
Bombus lucorum, **62**, 63, 68, 69, 84-87, see White-tailed bumblebee aggregate
Bombus. monticola, 63, **64**, 116-119 see Billberry/Blaeberry bumblebee
Bombus muscorum, 22, 41, 63, **65**, 124-127 see Moss carder bee
Bombus pascuorum, **62**, 63 120-123 see Common carder bee
Bombus pratorum, **62**, 69, 112-115 see Early bumblebee
Bombus ruderarius **65**, 107, 108-111 see Red-shanked carder bee
Bombus ruderatus, 24, 41, 63, **65**, 96-99 see Ruderal bumblebee
Bombus rupestris, 63, **64**, 152-155 see Red-tailed cuckoo bee
Bombus soroeensis, 63, 92-95 see Broken-belted bumblebee
Bombus subterraneus, 24, 25, 63, **65**, 100-103 see Short-haired bumblebee
Bombus sylvarum, 63, **65**, 132-135 see Shrill carder bee
Bombus sylvestris, 63, **64**, 156-159 see Forest cuckoo bee

Bombus terrestris, 23, 42, **62**, 63, 68, 69, 72-75, see Buff-tailed bumblebee
Bombus vestalis, 63, **64**, 140-143, see Southern cuckoo bee
Bottom thoracic band, **19**
Brush hairs, **18, 70**
Broken-belted bumblebee, 63, **64**, 92-95 see *Bombus soroeensis*
Brown-banded carder bee, 63, 128-131 see *Bombus humilis*,
Buff-tailed bumblebee, 23,62, 63, 72-75 see *Bombus terrestris*
Bumblebee, 12
Carder bees, 15
Cell, 13
Cocoon, 15, 17
Collecting information, 56-61
Colonies, 13, 45
Colony, 14, 15, 17, 42, 44, 52
Colour patterns, 21
Common carder bee, **62**, 120-123 see *Bombus pascuorum*
Cuckoo bees, 1, 62, 67, 68, 140 - 163
Cuckoo bumblebee, 15, 17, 64
Cullum's bumblebee, 24
Decline, 25, 39, 40, 42-45
Dig for victory, 43
Drones, 14
Early bumblebee, **62**, 112-115 see *Bombus pratorum*
Ecosystems, 37
Evolution, 26
Extinct species, 14
Exoskeleton, 20, 21
Eye, **19**
Face-lengths, 10, **71**
Field cuckoo bee, 63, **64**, 143, 144-147 see *Bombus campestris*
Filament, **35**
Flight muscles, 11, 38
Flying mouse, 22 see Patagonian bumblebee
Forest cuckoo bee, 63, 64, 156-159 see *Bombus sylvestris*
Fore wing, **18**
Fossilised bee, 26
Garden bumblebee, **62**, 63, 70, 76-79 see *Bombus hortorum*
Great Yellow bumblebee, 63, **65**, 136-139 see *Bombus distinguendus*
Gypsy cuckoo bee, 63, **64**, 148-151 see *Bombus bohemicus*
Heath bumblebee, 63, **64**, 78, 80-83 see *Bombus jonellus*
Habitat, creating new, 48-51
Habitat, loss, 40, 41, 43
Herbivores, 26
Hibernation, 17
High Arctic bumblebees, 22
Hind leg, 10, 21, **19**, **70**, 71
Hind wing, **18**
Hive, 12, 13, 14

Honey bee, 12, **13**, 14, 37
Identification, five steps to, 66
Larva, 13, 15,
Larvae, 13, 15, 16, 17, 44
Lifecycle, 13, 14, **16**, 17, 21
"Low input" approach, 41
Mandibles, 20
Mating, 12, 13, 14, 17,
Moss carder bee, 63, **65**, 124-127 see *Bombus muscorum*
Nectar, 10, 13, 15, 16, 17, 26, 32, 33, 35, 36, 37, 44, 46, 48 see tongue lengths
Nectary, **35**
Nest, 12, 13, 14, 15, **16,** 17, 21, 25, 29, 38, 41, 43, 44, 53, 61, 63
Neonicotinoids, 44
Ocelli, 20
Osmia bicornis, 13
Ovary, 34, **35**
Ovipositor, 20, 21
Ovule, **35**
Parasites, 23, 24, 45
Patagonian bumblebee, 22 see flying mouse
Plants, bee friendly, 42
Polar bumblebees, 22
Pollen, 10, 12, 13, 14, 15, 16, 26, 31, 32, 33, 34, 35, **36,** 37, 38, 44, 46, 48, 70
Pollen basket, 10, **18**, 20, 21, 38, 70, **71**
Pollination, 32, 35, 36, 37
Pollination, buzz, 38, **39**
Pollination, crop, 39
Pollination, insect, 34, **40**
Pollination, self, 39, **39**
Pollinators, 32, 33, 34, 37, 38, 39, 40, 41, 42
Population regulators, 45
Predators, 44, 45, 53
Pupa, 13, 15
Pupae, 12, 44
Red-shanked carder bee, **65**, 108-111 see also *Bombus ruderarius*
Red-tailed bumblebee, **62**, 104-107 see also *Bombus lapidarius*
Red-tailed cuckoo bee, **64**, 152-155 see also *Bombus rupestris*
Royal jelly, 13
Ruderal bumblebee, 23, **65**, 96-99 see also *Bombus ruderatus*
Sepal, **35**
Shrill carder bee, **65**, 132-135 see also *Bombus sylvarum*
Short-haired bumblebee, 23, 24, **65**, 100-103 see also *Bombus subterraneus*
Social,13, 15, 17, 21, 70, 71
Solitary bees, 12, 22
Sonication, 38
Southern cuckoo bee, 63, **64**, 140-143, see *Bombus vestalis*
Species, UK, 12

Stamen, 34, **35**
Stigma, 34, **35**
Sting, **19**, 20, 21, 30, 44, 52
Stings, un-barbed, 30
Subsidy system, 44
Swarming, 14
Tail, **18**
Tibia, **70, 71**
Thoracic band, **19**, **68-69**
Thorax, **18**, 20, 21,66 **68-69**
Tongue groups, 10
Tongue length, 10, 21
Transect, 59
Tree bumblebee, 25, **62**, 68, 63, 88-91 see *Bombus hypnorum*
Wasps, carnivorous, 26
Wildflower bed, how to make, 54-55
Wings, 29, 38,
White-tails, **67**, 72–103
White-tailed bumblebee, **62**, 63 84-87, see also *Bombus lucorum*
Wing muscles, 28, 29
Wings, 20, 21,29, 30, 38
Workers, 14, 15
Yellow-tailed cuckoo bee, **67**, 144-147